Songs of
the
Rivers of America

The Editor wishes to thank the following artists for their illustrations, which originally appeared in the Rivers of America series:

DAVID AND LOLITA GRANAHAN . UPPER MISSISSIPPI
ALEXANDER KEY . . . . THE SUWANNEE
ROSS SANTEE . . . . POWDER RIVER
JOHN O'HARA COSGRAVE II . . . THE SACRAMENTO
JOHN DE MARTELLY . . . . THE WABASH
DONALD McKAY . . . . THE ARKANSAS
AARON BOHROD . . . . THE ILLINOIS
ISABEL BATE AND HAROLD BLACK . . . THE KAW
ANDREW WYETH . . . . THE BRANDYWINE
ERNEST J. DONNELLY . . . . THE CHARLES
JOHN A. SPELMAN III . . . . . . THE KENTUCKY
HENRY C. PITZ . . . . THE ALLEGHENY
MAITLAND DE GOGORZA . . . . . THE KENNEBEC
A. Y. JACKSON . . . . THE ST. LAWRENCE
HARRY L. TIMMINS . . . . THE CHICAGO

Songs of the Rivers of America

Edited by CARL CARMER

Music Arranged by DR. ALBERT SIRMAY

New York · FARRAR & RINEHART, Inc. · Toronto

EDITOR'S NOTE

The following songs are reprinted by special permission as indicated.. As far as I know the songs which are not annotated with statements of permission and waiver of copyright are in the public domain. Every effort has been made to give credits where they are deserved. Many of the folk songs have been collected by the editor. Reproduction of them for commercial purposes should only be made after independent research.

C. C.

"El-a-noy," from *The American Songbag*, compiled by Carl Sandburg, copyright, 1927, by Harcourt, Brace & Company, Inc., and reprinted by their permission.

"Ida May," reprinted by permission of William A. Pond & Co., Ridgefield Park, New Jersey.

"Illinois," copyright, 1918, 1925, by Clayton F. Summy Co., New York and Chicago, and reprinted by their permission.

"Oh Honey, I'm Going Down the River," reprinted by permission of Associated Music Publishers, Inc., New York.

"Olban, or the White Captive," from Set 19 of Schirmer's American Folk Song Series, *Country Songs of Vermont*, collected by Helen Hartness Flanders, copyright, 1937, by G. Schirmer, Inc., and reprinted by their permission.

"Ole Pee Dee," and "Ole Tar River," from *Slave Songs of the Georgia Sea Islands*, copyright, 1942, by Lydia Parrish, and reprinted by her permission, and the permission of Creative Age Press, Inc., New York.

"On That Hill by the Tennessee," copyright, 1891, by William A. Pond & Co., and reprinted by their permission.

"On the Banks of the Old Pee Dee," "Stone River" and "The Wyandotte's Farewell Song," from *Ballads and Songs from Ohio*, copyright, 1939, by Mary O. Eddy, and reprinted by her permission.

"The Banks of the Genesee," copyright, 1923, by John Donoghue and A. A. Melville, and reprinted by their permission.

"The Housatonic Valley," reprinted by permission of the author, Clayton D. Stickles.

To Anne and Frank Warner
Singers on all our folk song trails

Contents

Editor's Foreword

On still summer evenings porch-sitters in Pascagoula, Mississippi, hear a deep melodic humming. The little river that flows by their houses and on past the wharves of the dark-sailed shrimp-boats is singing as it loses itself in the wide waters of the Gulf of Mexico.

The flags of eight governments have floated over this old town in its long history. Each has had its poets to tell why the Pascagoula sings. They have written too much to be set down here. But The "Singing River of the Gulf Coast" may well be thought a symbol of all the rivers of America.

For each of the shining strands of the harp-like water-web that lies across our land sings to us. Out of its valley rise the songs of the river that made it—songs of the explorers and voyageurs who used these open waters as highways, songs of the settlers sowing the rich bottom lands, songs of raft and flatboat, of keelboat and steam packet, bringing our harvests to market. River jobs and river games and the personal dramas of river living have made rhymes for us—and tunes for us to sing them to. So have our memories of the days of long ago in our valleys.

"A river is more than an amenity; it is a treasure," said Chief Justice Oliver Wendell Holmes, wording a decision of the Federal Supreme Court. He spoke for all the people of the United States of America.

The choosing of songs for this book has been both interesting and difficult. Some of the selections suggested themselves at once—the river songs of Stephen Foster, B. R. Hanby's "Darling Nelly Gray." Others were hard to find. A few came to my attention by accident and many were obtained only after extensive research.

Several songs appear here in print, so far as the editor knows, for the first time. A typical process in obtaining them is observable in my efforts to find the tune for "Old Butler's," sung long years ago by raftsmen on the Susquehanna. I had seen the words of the song in Professor Harold Thompson's admirable volume of New York State folklore, *Body, Boots and Britches*, and I wrote him asking for aid. He sent my letter on to a former member of his classes, Mr. Fred C. Mohrman of Sidney, New York. That gentleman generously spent some time in seeking out a resident of Hancock, New York—Mr. Charles T. White, when young the companion of many a raftsman. Mr. White remembered the tune and sang it to Miss Helen Conlon, a church organist in Hancock, who recorded the melody line and sent it to me. I fitted it to the words and gave it to Dr. Sirmay, who made the arrangement which is printed in this book. Much more rare was my experience with "Baby, Did You Hear?" which stevedores sing today on the banks of the St. Johns in Florida. This song came into the volume unsought through the volunteered interest and industry of Mr. Stetson Kennedy of Miami. Others of the variety unprinted until now came out of my own collection and from the more comprehensive files of the distinguished collector of folk songs, Mr. Frank Warner.

The songs of the rivers of America fall for the most part into four general categories. First of these are the songs of nostalgic yearning for the old days by the stream—like "Bonny Eloise, the Belle of the Mohawk Vale," or "The Banks of the Genesee." Songs of historical content make up a second classification, including "Brave Wolfe," "All Quiet Along the Potomac," "On that Hill by the Tennessee," and many others. The third group, comprising folk songs, is subdivided into songs inspired by jobs—like "The Shantyman's Life" (a lumberjack ditty) or the "Ogallaly Song" (a cowboy ballad)—and song-narratives of crimes committed by the river's side—like "Old Pee Dee," and "The Unconstant Lover." Fourth and last of the major divisions are the Minstrel Songs, composed in the mid-decades of the 19th Century for the traveling, blackface showmen and frequently celebrating a southern river for no other reason than that it made a fitting subject for a sentimental Negro-dialect song. Foster's song about the Ohio River steamboat *Glen D. Burke* ("The Glendy Burke") and "Poor Juna" well represent these. Certain other songs in the book are so individual as to defy facile listing.

In the course of the years some lyrics have been separated from the tunes they were sung to and one of my happiest research adventures has been in restoring the lost ones to each other. It was very exciting, for instance, after having spent many a despairing hour in seeking the tune of "The Banks of Brandywine" (the words of which I had found in George Jackson's scholarly *Early Songs of Uncle Sam*) to discover quite by chance (through identity of phrasing in certain stanzas) that it was sung to the same music as the old folk song "Ranordine."

By far the greater number of songs here published make definite mention of the river whose waters they praise or of places on its banks. Some songs have been included, however, in which no locale is named. In such cases notes are offered with the song explaining its close relationship to the river with which it is here associated.

Many of these songs, particularly those of folk origin, have many more stanzas than most people care to sing. In such cases only those stanzas which have especially to do with the river, or those stanzas which most effectively tell the events of a story-song, have been chosen.

A number of American colleges which stand on riverbanks have decorated their songs by references to the streams. These songs, the University of Rochester "Alma Mater"—"The Genesee," the Rutgers College song—"On the Banks of the Old Raritan" and others similar have been omitted as concerned primarily with college life rather than with the river they name.

The division of this book into three sections—Songs of the Rivers of the East, Songs of the Rivers of the South, Songs of the Rivers of the West—and the assignment of certain songs to each has been, of necessity, arbitrary. Several of the rivers run through at least two of the geographical regions named and I have been obliged to decide to which one their songs should be attributed. Since rivermen generally are inclined to designate any stream west of Pennsylvania and New York as "Western" I have allowed that category to include most rivers from the Susquehanna to the Sacramento.

Having collected old popular songs and folk songs for many years I am most gratefully aware of the mass of work done by other collectors and of its influence on my efforts. My knowing what to look for and where to look was unquestionably aided by my extensive reading in the song volumes of John and Alan Lomax, Carl Sandburg, David W. Bone, Margaret Larkin, Franz Rickaby, Jean Thomas, Mary O. Eddy, Joanna Colcord, H. M. Belden, Phillips Barry, Helen Hartness Flanders, Frank Shay, Sigmund Spaeth, Mrs. Maxfield Parrish, S. Foster Damon, Philip D. Jordan, Lillian Kessler, Elie Siegmeister and others.

Many friends have given me aid in finding the songs of the rivers and I am grateful to them all. I wish particularly to thank for wise and spirited counsel Franklin P. Adams, John Tasker Howard, Sigmund Spaeth, Frank Warner and, for comprehensive and imaginative research, Eloise Perry Hazard.

CARL CARMER

Introductory Notes About the Music

Folklore is fascinating. One can easily understand scientists and amateurs giving their whole lifetime to the research and analysis of folklore.

I spent a few months in arranging and editing the songs contained in this book. All this work was sheer pleasure.

It is true that Mr. Carmer's wide knowledge of American folk songs made my task very easy and simple. Thanks to him, I did not need to go through the country to discover songs; I did not need to coax people to sing for me. All I had to do was to follow Carl Carmer's friendly and erudite guidance among the chanting rivers and valleys of this country. The only trips I had to undertake were those to the rich shelves of the Music Division of the New York Public Library.

For me, as a musician, it was thrilling to study the files and books of American songs of the past. America is a young nation. Her musical folklore may not have the "patina" of other older nations. Perhaps American folk songs are not as delicate as those of France, not as sweet as Italy's, not as melancholy as Hungary's or as fiery and robust as Russia's songs. But American folk songs have something in common which cannot be surpassed by any other nation—something that permeates the surface of crudeness and brutality. They all have the refreshingly healthy spirit of a pioneering nation, a nation whose life for many generations involved continuous fight against merciless nature.

Most of these American songs exhale the captivating fragrance of an age which was much less complicated than ours. Not all of them are folk songs. Many have been written by well-known authors such as Stephen Foster, but most of them come straight out of American folklore.

No matter whether I found these songs in rough, irregular annotations of their melodies or supplied with harmonies, they all appear here in this book in my own arrangements. Even the traditionally best known printed songs I have rearranged for the piano, but throughout the book I persistently refrained from injuring their natural simplicity.

It is not difficult for a skilled musician to embellish any melody with the trimmings and ornaments of modern music. There are anthologies of folk songs which indulge in this modernizing process. Some of them do it beyond all measure.

I consider this a great mistake. I believe that the arrangement of a folk song should not transcend the limitations of the harmonic world familiar to the ears of a generation or several generations. This strict principle explains the simple harmonic structure of my piano accompaniments. And although these accompaniments always include the melody, I did my best to make them as easily playable as possible.

One more word about the way I adjusted the multitude of varied and irregular stanzas to the melody line. The prosody of folk songs is at times quite poor and arbitrary and here and there I have had to insert words against all metric laws. Many anthologies overcome this troublesome obstacle by printing the abundant stanzas on separate pages. In my opinion, placing all the words below the vocal line makes the reading or playing much more convenient and greatly increases the full enjoyment of the song.

Dr. Albert Sirmay

Songs of
the
Rivers of the East

WHITE settlers of cabin-towns along the eastern rivers found the Indians fierce and treacherous fighters in defense of their homes. Though the newcomers feared the arrow and the tomahawk they could not overcome, even within themselves, the popular 17th Century idea that the savage child of nature was possessed of extraordinary human virtues. Hence came many a sentimental recitation, many a song, like "Blue Juniata" or "Olban, the White Captive," devoted to revealing the noble qualities of the Indian.

We cut down the trees along the banks of our rivers and we floated the trunks of them downstream to be cut into boards to wall our houses. The Hudson's current is said to have been the first to have carried logs to a river sawmill. Thousands of American lumberjacks have worked in the snowy forests all winter long in order that the nation might have wood. Many a song has been born to the rhythmic swing of their axes and roared out again at night in the smoky bunkhouse.

Our first cities grew up on the banks of our eastern rivers and the songs that have been written about them, like "Niagara Falls," "New York, Oh what a Charming City," relate social history quite as well as any scholarly studies of early city life.

Have You Struck Ile?

(Allegheny, 1865)

Joseph B. Quinby
Tune: "The Irish Jaunting Car"
Arranged by "A Speculator"

The discovery of oil in the Allegheny valley in the summer of 1859 resulted in the fantastic growth of towns like Oil City, Pennsylvania, and in incredible riches for such picturesque characters as John W. Steele, known to most of the world of his time as "Coal Oil Johnnie." Striking oil also resulted in the writing of such topical songs as this one.

Lightly

1. From Cal - i - for - nia o - cean laved, To old Vir - gin - ia shore,____ And from the gulf of Mex - i - co, To North - ern Lab - ra - dor,____ All o'er the land the word is now, Pe -
2. Brown says to Jones: "Have you struck ile?" And Jones in turn asks Brown,____ so the ques - tion goes a - long Through coun - ty, state and town,____ Pe - tro - le - um's the new - born wealth, which
3. But yes - ter - day that man was poor, Who's now a mil - lion - aire,____ For on his lands deemed worth - less then, are found oil - wells most rare,____ His neigh - bors all, now half run mad, are
4. All hail! the new - born wealth, all hail! Now gush - ing from oil foun - tains,____ In ev - 'ry part of our proud land, from val - leys, plains and moun - tains,____ We've wealth un - told, in oil and gold, rich

poco a poco cresc.   *mp*   *mf*   *p*   *poco a poco cresc.*

tro - leum all the while, _____ And all the bor - ers
is - sues from the soil, _____ And th'all ab - sorb - ing
bor - ing through the soil, _____ And ol - ea - gin - ous
trea - sures in our soil, _____ What care we if all

mf

and the bores in - quire: "Have you struck Ile?" _____
ques - tion now's: "My friend have you struck Ile?" _____
signs they seek, all hop - ing to strike Ile. _____
Eu - rope rage, our Na - tion has struck Ile!

Refrain

Hur - rah! _____ Hur - rah! _____ Rich treas - ures in our sile, _____ What

f

care we if all Eu - rope rage, Our Na - tion has struck Ile. _____

4

The Banks of the Brandywine

Placidly

mp

1. One— morn - ing ver - y—
2. At— such an ear - ly
3. She— said: "Young man be—
4. "Oh— no, my dear, that—

ear - ly, in the pleas-ant month of May, As I walked forth to—
hour— I— was sur-prised to see, A— love-ly maid with
civ - il, my— com-pan-y for-sake, For— in my real o—
ne'er shall be, be— hold your Hen - ry now, I'll— clasp you to my—

take the air, All na - ture be - ing gay. The moon had not yet—
down-cast eyes Up - on those banks so gay. I mod - est - ly sa - id
pin - i - on, I think you are a rake; My love's a val - iant—
bos - om, love, I've not for - got my vow; It's now I know you're

cresc.

veil'd her face, but through the trees did shine, As I
lut - ed her, she knew not my de - sign, And re -
sail - or, he's now gone to the main, Now
true, my dear, in Hy - men's chains we'll join, As I

wan - dered for a muse - ment, On the banks of Bran - dy - wine.
quest - ed her sweet com - pan - y, On the banks of Bran - dy - wine.
I'm a maid for - sak - en, On the banks of Bran - dy - wine."
hail the hap - py morn we met, On the banks of Bran - dy - wine."

The Bridge

(Charles, 1845)

Words by Henry Wadsworth Longfellow
Music by M. Lindsay

Extracts from the Journal of Henry Wadsworth Longfellow for 1845 read: "October 9th—Finished 'The Bridge over the Charles'" ... "October 17th—Retouched 'The Bridge.'"

Meditatively

1. I stood on the bridge at mid-night, As the clocks were strik-ing the hour, And the moon rose o'er the cit-y, Be-hind the dark church tow'r. And like the wa-ters rush-ing A-mong the wood-en piers, A flood of thoughts came

2. For my heart was hot and rest-less, And my life was full of care, And the bur-den laid up-on me Seem'd great-er than I could bear. But now it has fall-en from me, It is bur-ied in the sea, And on-ly the sor-row of

o'er me That filled my eyes with tears, How

oth - ers Throws its shad - ow o - ver me; Yet when -

oft - en oh! how oft - en, In the days that had gone

ev - er I cross the riv - er, On its bridge with wood - en

by, I had stood on that bridge at mid - night And

piers, Like the o - dor of brine from the o - cean Comes the

gazed on wave and sky! How oft - en, oh, how oft - en, In the

thought of oth - er years, And for - ev - er, and for - ev - er, As

Ben Bolt

(Delaware, 1843)

Words by Thomas Dunn English
Old German Melody

Editor Nathaniel Parker Willis requested Thomas Dunn English to write a sea poem for publication in the New York *Mirror*. English, lacking inspiration for the subject, could think only of his happy boyhood days on his ancestral acres, "The English Farm," in the Delaware valley and wrote this nostalgic verse-letter to an old friend. Later a young actor, Nelson Kneass, seeking a song to use in a tryout appearance for a stock company, set it to his own adaptation of an old German melody.

1. Oh, don't you re-mem-ber, sweet Al-ice, Ben Bolt, Sweet Al-ice with hair so brown, She wept with de-light when you gave her a smile, And trem-bled with fear at your frown. In the old church-yard, in the val-ley, Ben Bolt, In a

2. Oh, don't you re-mem-ber, the wood, Ben Bolt, Near the green sun-ny slope of the hill, When oft we have sung 'neath its wide spreading shade, And kept time to the click of the mill. The mill has gone to de-cay, Ben Bolt, And a

cor - ner ob - scure and a - lone.
qui - et now reigns all a - round.

They have fit - ted a slab of—
See the old rus - tic porch with its

poco rit. *p a tempo*

gran - ite so grey, And sweet Al - ice lies un - der the stone.
ros - es so sweet, Lies— scat - ter'd and fall'n to the ground.

They have
See the

mf

fit - ted a slab of— gran - ite so grey And sweet Al - ice lies un - der the stone.
old rus - tic porch, with its ros - es so sweet, Lies— scat - ter'd and fall'n— to the ground.

dimin. e rit.

Michael Roy

(East)

In a happy mood

1. In Brook - lyn Cit - y there lived a maid, And
2. She fell in love with a char - coal man, Mc -

she was known to fame,_____ Her moth - er's name was
Clos - key was his name,_____ His fight - ing weight was

Ma - ry Ann, And hers was Ma - ry Jane;_____ And
sev - en - stone ten, And he loved sweet Ma - ry Jane;_____ He

ev - 'ry Sat - ur - day morn - ing She
took her to ride in his char - coal cart On a

used to go o - ver the riv - er, ___ And went to mar - ket where
fine St. Pat - rick's day, ___ But the don-key took fright at a

she sold eggs And sas - sa - ges, like - wise liv - er. ___
Jer - sey man And start - ed and ran a - way. ___

Refrain

For oh! ___ For oh! ___ he was my dar - ling boy, ___ For

he was the lad with the au - burn hair, And his name was Mich - ael Roy. ___

Strolling o'er the Brooklyn Bridge

(East, 1883)

Words by George Cooper
Music by J. P. Skelly

Not fast, but gaily

o'er the Brook-lyn Bridge we roam, When moon-light tints the sea._
on the Brook-lyn Bridge we meet, I and my dar-ling true._
walks be-neath the moon-lit sky, Where first my love I met._

Refrain

Strol-ling o'er the Brook-lyn Bridge, Dream-y hours go by,____ Whisp-'ring words of fond de-light 'Neath the star-ry sky.____ Hap-py as the

danc - ing waves, Hearts are lost and won; We fond - ly stray with

hearts so gay Up - on the Brook - lyn Bridge. 2. Some Bridge..
3. 'Twas

Flat River Girl

The Flat River flows near Greenville, Maine,
at the foot of Moosehead Lake.

Emphatically, but not fast

mf

1. Come all you fine young
2. Her form was like the
3. She was a black- smith's
4. To her moth - er Jane

fel - lows with hearts so warm and true, —
dove, __ so slen - der and so neat, Her
daugh - ter from the Flat __ Riv - er side, And
Tuck - er, I lay __ all the blame, —

Nev - er be - lieve in a wom - an, You're lost __ if you
long brown chest - nut curls hung to her __ tin - y
I al - ways had in - tend - ed for to make __ her my
She caused her to leave me And to black - en my

do. But if you ev - er see one with

feet. Her voice it was like mu - sic or

bride; But one day on the riv - er a

name. I count - ed her my dar - ling, what a

long brown chest - nut curls, Just think of Jack ___

mur - murs of the breeze As she whis - pered that she

let - ter I re - ceived; She said that from her

la - dy for wife, When I think of her

Hag - ger - ty and his Flat Riv - er girl. ___

loved me as we strolled a - mong the trees. ___

prom - ise her - self she had re - lieved. ___

treach - er - y it near - ly takes my life. ___

The Banks of the Genesee

(1923)

Words by John Donoghue
Music by A. A. Melville

Softly

1. I played up-on your banks, a wild bare-foot boy   And
2. (I) love the dear old folks who live on your shore   A-

swam through your streams, My heart full of joy, Though gone are my com-rades, Who
gain bright sea-gulls a-round you they soar   Like an-gels from heav-en, Watch

joined in my glee___ Their sweet fac-es re-flect   In you Gen-e-
o'er you and me And the peo-ple that live on the old Gen-e-

Refrain (*slowly*)

see.
see.   Roll a-long___ grand old riv-er vis-ion of

dreams,____ Take me back to my boy-hood near the fin-est of streams____ They may sing of the Shan-non, the Lif-fey and Lee,____ But I dream of the grand-eur of you Gen-e-see.____ 2. I see.____

The Vale of Our Own Genesee

H. P. Danks

With nostalgic sentiment

1. All na-ture with beau-ty is teem-ing,— The soft breeze is fan-ning my
2. The moun-tains the sun-set is gild-ing,— Are tow'r-ing in gran-deur sub-
3. When life with its tur-moil is end-ed, And glad-ly I sink to my

brow;— But I gaze half ad-mir-ing, half dream-ing,— For my
lime:— And green are the hills and the val-leys,— Of this
rest,— One thought of the past will be blend-ed,— With

spir-it is wan-der-ing now,— Far back to the loved haunts of
balm-y, this soft gen-tle clime,— But the hills and the glens and the
e-ven the hope of the blest;— Oh,— then when the home of im-

child-hood, The home where I part-ed from thee;— O there's
wild-wood, On earth that are dear-est to me,— En-
mor-tals, Is op'-ning its por-tals for me,— Make

noth-ing on earth half so love-ly, — As the vale of our own Gen-e - see. —
cir-cle the home of my child-hood, — The vale of our own Gen-e - see. —
room for the frail, emp-ty cas-ket, — In the vale of our own Gen-e - see. —

Refrain

mp legato

Oh, the vale of our own Gen-e - see, — Yes, the

vale of our own Gen-e - see, — There's noth-ing on earth half so

mf

love - ly, As the vale of our own Gen-e - see. —

poco rit.

The Housatonic Valley

Words by Clayton E. Stickles
Melody: "The Vacant Chair"
by G.F. Root

1. As the eve-ning sha-dows length-en And all na-ture is at rest, All my thoughts are turn-ing back there To the place I love the best. Oh, that qui-et, peace-ful

2. I still see the lit-tle cot-tage, Nes-tled in that Berk-shire dell, Where the birds were al-ways sing-ing, 'Round the home we loved so well. All was joy and nev-er

3. Since I left this love-ly val-ley, Left a home and all be-hind, I'm a wand-'rer of the waste-land, Nev-er more in peace of mind. But I soon will go back

val - ley That I left so long a - go, Where we
sor - row, In this E - den of the blest, And we
yon - der, For I know she'll wait - ing be, In the

sat and dreamed to - geth - er, Watched the Hou - sa - ton - ic flow.
knew that each to - mor - row Would bring peace and per - fect rest.
Hou - sa - ton - ic val - ley, There'll be joy for her and me.

Refrain (*slowly*)

As the eve - ning shad - ows length-en And all na - ture is at rest, All my

thoughts are turn - ing back there, To the place I love the best.

poco rit.

This ballad in its original form contained over forty stanzas. It is based on a true incident which occurred in Berlin, New York. Professor Louis C. Jones of Albany State Teachers' College has done an excellent monograph on it. Helen Hartness Flanders and George Brown present a version in their *Vermont Folk Songs and Ballads.*

The Ballad of Henry Green

(Hudson)

With proper melancholy

1. Come lis-ten to my trag-e-dy, Good peo-ple young and old;— I'll tell you of a sto-ry 'Twill make your blood run cold,— Con-cern-ing a fair dam-sel, Miss Wy-att was her name;—She was mur-dered by her hus-band And he hung for the same.—

2. Great doc-tors they were sent for, but none of them could save,— And soon by them it was pro-claimed she must go to her grave.— Young Hen-ry Green was sent for, locked up in Troy— Jail,—There to a-wait his tri-al; the court could not take bail.—

3. "Now Hen-ry has de-ceived me, how my poor heart is wrung,— But when I'm dead and bur-ied, don't have poor Hen-ry hung;— I free-ly have for-giv-en him," And she turned up-on her side,— "In heav-en meet me, Hen-ry," and she sweet-ly smiled and died.—

4. Now he ap-peared to be un-moved, and still he was so young,— Judge Bak-er read the sen-tence, he said he must be hung,— He said when au-tumn leaves turn and sum-mer days have fled,— He too must close his youth-ful life and slum-ber with the dead.—

poco rit.

Benny Havens, Oh!

(Hudson)

Benny Havens, 1st lieutenant in the War of 1812, retired from the service to run a grog shop at Highland Falls, New York. In 1838 "Lieutenant O'Brien" of the Eighth Infantry wrote this song to celebrate West Point's favorite rendezvous.

Lieutenant O' Brien
Tune: "Wearing Of The Green"

Very sonorously and not fast

1. Come fill your glass-es, fel-lows, and stand up in a row, To sing-ing sen-ti-men-tal-ly we're go-ing for to go; In the ar-my there's so-bri-e-ty, pro-mo-tion's ver-y slow, So we'll sing our rem-i-nis-cenc-es of Ben-ny Ha-vens, oh!

2. To our kind old Al-ma Ma-ter, our rock-bound High-land home, We'll cast back man-y a fond re-gret as our life's sea we roam; Un-til on our last bat-tle-field the lights of heav-en glow, We'll nev-er fail to drink to her and Ben-ny Ha-vens, oh!

3. May the ar-my be aug-ment-ed, pro-mo-tion be less slow, May our coun-try in the hour of need be read-y for the foe. May we find a sol-dier's rest-ing place be-neath a sol-dier's blow, With room e-nough be-side our graves for Ben-ny Ha-vens, oh!

Oh— Ben-ny Ha-vens, oh,— Oh Ben-ny Ha-vens, oh, We'll

sing our rem-i-nis-cenc-es of Ben-ny Ha-vens, oh!

The Hudson Side

As sung by Miss Julia W. Pomeroy in the romantic opera, "The Miser's Well," produced in New York in the early 1840s.

Edward Fitzball
G. Herbert Rodwell

With sure and easy rhythm

1. Oh, I could pic-ture a hap-py lot, In some lit-tle cot, by the Hud-son side. Our lone-ly seat_ where wil-lows meet,_ To dip their leaves in the sil-ver tide, Oh, I could pic-ture a hap-py lot, In some lit-tle cot, by the Hud-son side. Our lone-ly seat_ where wil-lows

2.(Up with the) sun, like the lark we'll be, At our ear-ly meal, on the vel-vet green. The murm'ring waves,_ wild mel-o-dy, With its mu-sic sweet, shall en-chant the scene. Up with the sun like the lark we'll be, At our ear-ly meal on the vel-vet green. The murm-'ring waves_ wild mel-o-

meet_ To dip their leaves in the sil - ver tide; On moss - y banks we'll pass the
dy, With its mu - sic sweet shall en - chant the scene; Yes bless'd, how bless'd, my hap-py

hours, And watch the white sails as they glide, Or bear bright
lot, My whole life long with my love - ly bride, Where ev - 'ry

wreaths of balm - y flow'rs, To our lit - tle cot on the Hud - son
care would be for - got,_ In our lit - tle cot on the Hud - son

side,_ Or bear bright wreaths of balm - y flow'rs To our lit - tle cot, our lit-tle
side,_ Where ev - 'ry care_ would be for - got, In our lit - tle cot, our lit-tle

cot, on ____ the Hud-son side. }
cot, on ____ the Hud-son side. } Oh I could pic-ture a hap-py

lot, In some lit-tle cot, by the Hud-son side. Our lone-ly seat _ where wil-lows

meet, _ To dip their leaves _ in the sil-ver tide, in the sil - ver,

sil - ver, sil - ver tide. 2. Up with the tide. _

This lumberjack ballad was sung to the editor
by "Yankee John" Galusha, octogenarian
lumberjack of the upper Hudson.

Joe Thomas
(Hudson)

In spirited, narrative mood

1. He said he'd been a boat-man for
2. It was on a Sun-day morn-ing just
3. The cur-rent was swift and nim-ble from the
4. He'd both-ered Nor-ton all spring to

six-teen year or more   He'd run the Hud-son Riv-er where the
at the hour of ten   Joe Thom-as and his boat crew their
jam she swept a-way   And spite of all that Joe could do for the
let him run the boat,   I guess he got his fill of her when from

thun-der-ing tor-rents pour___ He dread nor feared no dan-ger while
bus-i-ness did be-gin,___ He slammed his boat a-gainst the jam and
cel-lar she made a-way,___ I guess she done some bus-i-ness that
him__ she did float,___ For his boat lays on the bot-tom and her

in his own ca - noe   He'd   run   the   Hud - son
split   her   bow   in   two   And   soon   she   filled   with
kept   her   bus - y   there   For   she   turned   a   hand - some
rig - ging's   cast   a - way.   Joe's   break - ing   jams   a -

Riv - er   And   the   In - dian   Riv - er   too.
wa - ter   And   washed   a - way   his   crew.
som - er - sault   And   her   bow   stood   in   the   air.
long   the   shore   For   a   dol - lar 'n' half   a   day.

Refrain

Watch her,   catch her,   jump her ju - ber - jew, —   Give her the wind and

let her go,   if   Joe can shove her   through. —   You ought to heard 'em

howl-in' as they went float-in' by With face the col-or of

snow, my boys, and a tear in ev-'ry eye.

rall. e dim.

Johnny Has Gone for a Soldier

(Hudson)

Originally an Irish song of the 1690s, "Johnny Has Gone for a Soldier" was popular in America during the Revolution. It has had many titles, including "Shule Aroon," and "On and On." John and Lucy Allison ascribe it to the Hudson valley in their admirable pamphlet which accompanies the record album of songs of their collection, *Songs of the Revolution and the War of 1812.*

Plaintively, but not too slowly

1. Oh, Johnny dear has gone away, He has gone afar across the bay, Oh, my heart is sad and weary today, Since Johnny has gone for a soldier.
2. I'll sell my flax, I'll sell my wheel, I'll buy my love a sword of steel, So to the battle he may reel; Oh, Johnny has gone for a soldier.
3. I wish I was on yonder hill, It's there I'd sit and cry my fill, So ev'ry tear may turn a mill, Oh, Johnny has gone for a soldier.
4. I'll dye my dress, I'll dye it red, And through the streets I'll beg my bread, Oh, how I wish that I were dead, Since Johnny has gone for a soldier.

Refrain

Schule, schule, schule a-grah, Time can only ease my woe, Since the lad of my heart from me did go, Oh, Johnny has gone for a soldier.

New York, Oh What a Charming City

"A favorite new ballad" in the 1850s.

(Hudson, pre-Civil War)

J. Gairdner

Very cheerfully

1. The ar - dent, ro - man - tic, The charm-ing God of song, Cross'd late - ly th'At - lan - tic Nor thought the voy - age long; He tripped a - long in shoes of cork, Sing-ing man - y a dit - ty, But he chang'd his song when he reach'd New York, To what a charm - ing cit - y.

2. In Bow - ery, in Broad-way, He ram - bled up and down, Took by - way and odd - way, Re - solved to see the town, And as he went, he sung this song, "Now, is it not a pi - ty" I should have stayed a - way so long From such a charm - ing cit - y.

3. Here Free-dom and du - ty, And truth and taste re - main, Here hon - our and beau - ty, And love and val - our reign; Here hith - er Free-dom's friends re - sort, The grave, the gay, the wit - ty, For here I'll hence - forth keep my court, In this de - light-ful cit - y.

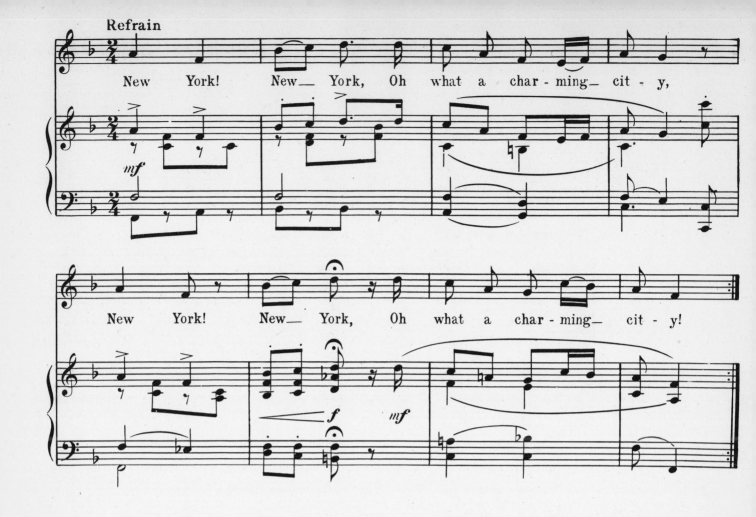

New York! New York, Oh what a char-ming cit-y,

New York! New York, Oh what a char-ming cit-y!

The Shantyman's Life

(Hudson)

This song appearing in the volumes of John and Alan Lomax, Carl Sandburg, Franz Rickaby and Phillips Barry is here given as sung by "Yankee John" Galusha.

In a robust, natural manner

1. Oh, a shan-ty-man's life is a wear-i-some life, al-though some think it void of care,_____ When we're swing-ing an ax from__ morn-ing till night in the midst of the for-ests so

2. (It's trans)-port-ed I am from the tame haunts of man, to the banks of the Hud-son drear,_____ Where the wolves and the owls with their ter-ri-ble howls, in-ter-fere with__ ev-'ry night-ly

3. (Oh, the) cook ris-es up in the midst of the night, say-ing "Hur-rah brave boys, it's day"_____ So our brok-en__ slum-bers__ oft-times are passed as the cold win-ter nights while a-

4. (And when) spring does set in our__ hard-ships be-gin, when the wa-ters are pierc-ing cold,_____ And our clothes are__ drip-ping wet and fin-gers be-numbed and our pike-poles we scarce-ly can

drear. _____ Ly - ing in the shan - ty _____ bleak and _____
dream, _____ Oh, the Shan-ty - man is the lad I love
way, _____ There's no rum, wine or _____ beer our
hold, _____ Be - tween _____ rock, shoals and sands make hard

cold, while the cold storm - y, win - t'ry _____ winds blew, And as
best, and I nev - er will de - ny the _____ 'same, _____ My
spir - its for to cheer all en - joy-ment we've left far be - hind, And there's
go - in' for all hands _____ our well brand-ed raft _____ for to steer, And the

soon as the day - light doth ap - pear, to the wild woods
heart it does de - spise those fool-ish cit - y boys who _____ think it a dis -
no one here to wipe a-way each tear when sor - row _____ fills our _____
rap - ids that we run, they seem to us but fun, for we're void of all

we must go. _____   2. It's trans -
grace - ful name. _____   3. Oh, the
troub - led mind. _____   4. And when
slav - ish fear. _____

38

This song was first published in the English
volume, *The Skylark*, in 1825 and later in
America in a collection called *The Singer's
Companion* which made its appearance in 1857.

The Weeping Willow

(Hudson, circa 1825)

Slowly and tenderly

1. Where Hud-son's murm-'ring bil-lows, Kiss Jer-sey's ver-dant shore, Be-neath the spread-ing wil-lows, Sleeps Hen-ry of the moor; The pride of all the plain, Was An-na's chos-en swain, But

2. They hail'd the brid-al mor-row, Which dawned to see them blest, But oh! ere eve, what sor-row Filled An-na's gen-tle breast! She saw the Hud-son's wave Be-come her Hen-ry's grave! And

3. She saw be-neath the wil-low Her Hen-ry laid to rest, The earth his nup-tial pil-low, And not her art-less breast! A-round his moss-y tomb The ear-ly dais-ies bloom, There

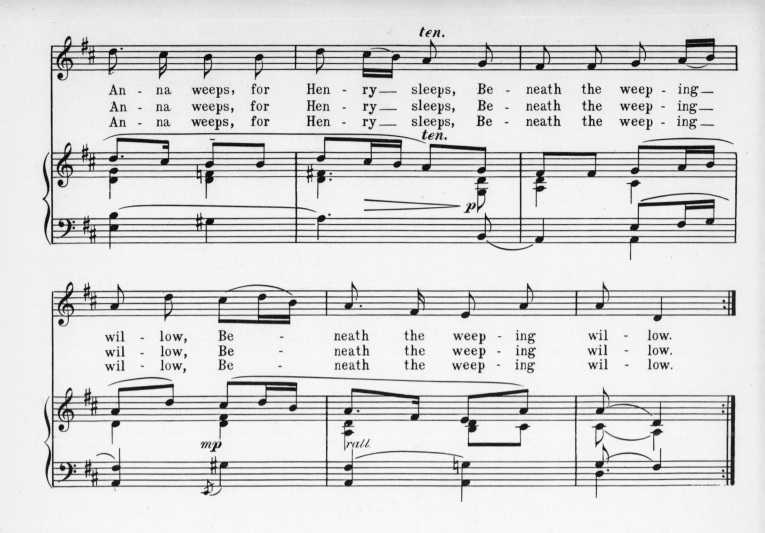

An - na weeps, for Hen - ry — sleeps, Be - neath the weep - ing —
An - na weeps, for Hen - ry — sleeps, Be - neath the weep - ing —
An - na weeps, for Hen - ry — sleeps, Be - neath the weep - ing —

wil - low, Be - neath the weep - ing wil - low.
wil - low, Be - neath the weep - ing wil - low.
wil - low, Be - neath the weep - ing wil - low.

Where Hudson's Wave

(Circa 1839)

Words by
G. P. Morris

Music by
Joseph Philip Knight

Where Hud-son's wave o'er sil-v'ry sands, Winds through the hills a - far, Old crow-nest like a mon-arch stands, Crown'd with a sin-gle star! ___ And there a - mid the bil - low-y swells_ Of rock ribb'd, cloud-capt earth ___ My fair and gen-tle I - da dwells,_ A nymph of moun-tain_ birth. ___ My

fair and gen-tle I-da dwells,— A nymph of moun-tain birth.— The snowflake that the cliff re-

ceives,— The dia-monds of the show'rs— Spring's ten-der blos-soms, buds and

leaves,— The sis-ter-hood of flow'rs,— Morn's ear-ly beam, eve's balm-y

breeze,— Her pur-i-ty de-fine,— But I-da's dear-er far than

these__ To this fond breast__ of mine.__ But I - da's dear-er far than

these To__ this fond breast of__ mine.__

Suddenly fast and passionately

My heart____ is on the hills,_ The shades of night are on my brow;_ Ye

pleas - ant haunts and si - lent glades, __ My soul is with you now! __ I

bless the star crown'd high-lands where_ My I - da's foot - steps_ roam:_

Oh! for a fal - con's wing to bear, to bear me on-ward to my home,_

Oh!_ for a fal - con's wing to bear, to bear me on-ward to my home,_ To bear me

on - ward to my home,_ To bear me on - ward to my home._

The Blue Juniata

(1844)

Mrs. Marion Dix Sullivan

1. Wild roved an In-dian girl, ___ Bright Al - fa - ra - ta,
2. Gay was the moun-tain song of Bright Al - fa - ra - ta,
3. Bold is my war - rior good, The love of Al - fa - ra - ta,
4. So sang the In - dian girl, ___ Bright Al - fa - ra - ta,

Where sweep the wa - ters of the blue ___ Ju - ni - a - ta.
Where sweep the wa - ters of the blue ___ Ju - ni - a - ta.
Proud waves his snow - y plume A - long the Ju - ni - a - ta.
Where sweep the wa - ters of the blue ___ Ju - ni - a - ta.

Swift as an an - te - lope, Through the for - est go - ing,
Strong and true my ar - rows are, In my paint - ed quiv - er,
Soft and low he speaks to me, And then his war - cry sound - ing,
Fleet - ing years have born a - way, The voice of Al - fa - ra - ta,

Loose were her pret - ty locks, In wa - vy tress - es flow - ing.
Swift goes my light ca - noe A - down the rap - id riv - er.
Rings his voice in thun - der loud, From height to height re - sound - ing.
Still sweeps the riv - er on, Of the blue ___ Ju - ni - a - ta.

Down in the Lehigh Valley

(Lehigh)

Originally a recitation of the late 19th Century and later set to this music, "Down in the Lehigh Valley" has become one of the most notorious of all bawdy American folk songs. These are the original (and only printable) words.

Somewhat pathetically

1. Down in the Le - high Val - ley,
2. Then came a friend - ly strang - er,
3. Well it's the same old sto - ry,
4. Back to our home we brought her,

Me and my peo - ple grew, I was the vil - lage black-smith And a
Hand - some straight and tall, Oh damn him, wish I had him A -
Com - mon e - nough you'll say, That smooth tongued dev - il fooled us And he
Back to her moth - er's side, Filled with a rag - ing fev - er She

gol - darn good one too. Me and my wife and
stood up a - gainst that wall, He was the man for
got her to run a - way. Less than a short month
fell at our feet and died. Give me a drink bar -

Nell - ie,   Nell - ie was just six - teen   She
Nell - ie,   We   She did - n't know no ill,   Her
lat - er,   We heard from the poor young thing,   He'd
ten - der,   And I will be on my way,   To

was the pret - ti - est crea - ture That the val - ley had ev - er seen. ____
moth - er tried to stop it, But you know a ____ young girl's will. ____
gone a - way and left her And with - out a ____ wed - ding ring. ____
kill the pal that stole my gal, If it takes un - til judge - ment day. ____

rit.

Jim Brown

(Merrimac)

land at War - ren Bridge, de mu - sic in my hand,
plays up - on de mu - sic when I_____ goes to war, I
plays up - on de mu - sic, I make de - han - som sound, I
Says he "Jim Brown what can you do_____ for_____ me?" "I

Quick I get de lead - er ob de famed___ brass___ band.
am de raft - iest ole nig - ger dat eb - er you saw.
am de mu - si - cian dat dey call___ Jim___ Brown."
can go in de gar - den and plant a hick', - ry tree." } Tat,

tat, tat, tat, tan, tat, ta - tat tan - ta - ta - tan tat, tat

tat, tat, tat, tat, tat, tat, tat, tat, ta - tat, ta - tat tan.

Olban, or the White Captive

(Merrimac)

The Rev. Thomas C. Upham
(Old Folk Tune: "The Golden Glove")

Smoothly moving

1. The moon had gone down o'er the hills of the west, And her last beam had fad-ed o'er Moose hill-lock's crest; 'Twas a mid-night of__ hor-ror the red me-te-or flash'd, And hoarse down the moun-tain the__ ca-ta-ract__ dash'd.

2. (Ere) blush-es of morn-ing a-gain should re-turn, In tor-ture A-man-da was des-tined to burn, A-man-da__ the__ pride of her vil-lage and home, Who__ far up the Mer-ri-mac's wa-ters had come.

3. (The) fag-gots were kind-led, the red torch-es glar'd, Her hands they were bound and her white bos-om bar'd; A-round her stood__ wait-ing the mer-ci-less throng, Im-pa-tient to join__ the war-dance and song.

4. (Young) Ol-ban, the chief of the war-riors was near, With the eye of an eag-le, the foot of the deer, And a soul that__ would__ scorn from a foe-man to crave, A__ sigh for his suff'rings, a__ tear for his grave.

1.-2.-3.: 2. Ere 3. The 4. Young

4.: 5. "For- 6. (To the) 7. (On) 8. (At)

From Set 19 of Schirmer's American Folk Song Series, *Country Songs of Vermont*, collected by Helen Hartness Flanders, copyright, 1937, by G. Schirmer, Inc., and reprinted by their permission.

bear" cried their chief - tain "your tor - tures for - bear The
arms of A - man - da, as for - ward he rush'd, The
Pe - mige was set, at dawn - ing of day, Their
dusk of the eve - ning the white cot was seen, And its

cap - tive shall live by this Wam - pum I swear, This
re - vel - ry ceased and the tu - mult was hush'd, And
birch - en ca - noe was seen glid - ing a - way, And
smoke curl - ing blue 'round the wild wil - low green; One

night if a vic - tim must burn at the tree, Young
mute stood the cir - cle of war - riors a - round, While
fleet as the wild duck, that swam by their side, In
mo - ment in part - ing they pass'd on the shore, And

5.-6.-7.   8.

Ol - ban, your lead - er, that vic - tim shall be." 5. To the
Ol - ban the chains of the cap - tive un - bound. 6. On
si - lence they rode down the dark roll - ing - tide. 7. At
Ol - ban the war - rior was heard of no more.

51

Bonny Eloise

(Mohawk, 1858)

This was one of the most popular songs of both warring armies during the War Between the States. It is said that the girl who inspired it was Mary Bowen of Fort Plain, New York.

Words by C. W. Elliott
Music by J. R. Thomas

Slow and sentimental

1. O,— sweet is the vale where the Mo-hawk gent-ly glides, On its clear wind-ing way to the sea, And— dear-er than all sto-ried streams on earth be-sides, Is this bright roll-ing riv-er to me._____ But

2. O,— sweet are the scenes of my boy-hood's sun-ny years, That be-span-gle the gay val-ley o'er, And— dear are the friends seen thro' mem-o-ries fond tears That have lived in the blest days of yore._____

Buffalo Gals

(Niagara)

Cool White

Gay and cocky

1. As I was lumb-'ring down de street,
2. I stopt her an' I had some talk,
3. She's de pret-ti-est gal I be seen in my life,
4. Oh, make haste, Fan, don't make me wait,

Down de street, down de street, A pret-ty gal I
Had some talk, had some talk, But her foot cov-ered up the
Seen in my life, seen in my life, An' I wish to de Lord she
Make me wait, make me wait, I fear you've kept me

chanc'd to meet, Oh, she was fair to view.
whole side-walk An' left no room for me.
was my wife, Den we would part no more.
now too late, Yes, dere's de ebe-ning gun.

Refrain

Den Buf-fa-lo gals will you cum out to-night, will you

54

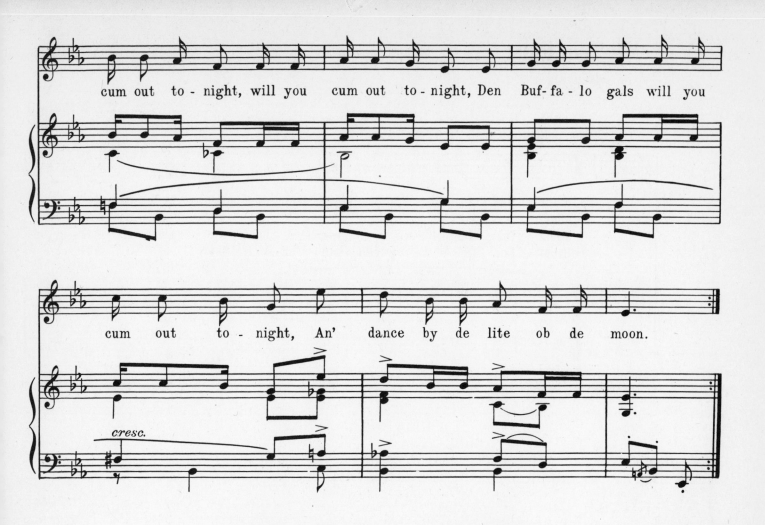

cum out to - night, will you cum out to - night, Den Buf-fa-lo gals will you

cum out to - night, An' dance by de lite ob de moon.

cresc.

Niagara Falls

(Niagara)

W. Winchell

Animatedly

1. From Buf - fa - lo my la - bour done, For cu - ri - os - i
2. The driv - er did his hors - es crack, Go - ing to Ni - ag -
3. Midst foam - ing bil -lows at length we land, On cakes of rock - y
4. Stuck fast in mud with sad tur -moil, Some lost a shoe a -

ty and fun, I took the cars, the morn - ing run, To
a - ra Falls; At length we ar - rived in time to dine, The
ice and stand, We all got safe up - on the strand, Go -
midst the toil, At length we reach'd the top - most soil, That

go to Ni - ag - a - ra Falls, sirs. The morn was cold the
Cat - a - ract Ho - tel is fine, sirs. We'd flesh and fish of
ing to Ni - ag - a - ra Falls, sirs. We gazed up - on the
leads to Ni - ag - a - ra Falls, sirs. The riv - al cat - a -

snow fell fast, Old Bor - eas blew a pip - ing blast, With
ev - 'ry kind And Ne - gro wait - ers to stand be - hind; The
Eng - lish Falls, _____ Tum - bling o - ver na - ture's walls; The
racts in view, _____ Roar - ing and rush - ing ev - er new; Goat

two horse pow'r set off at last, We'd pas - sen - gers_ of
land - lord he pro - cured a guide, Who took us down_ to
noise of which your heart ap - palls, Just like the thou - sand
Is - land stands be - twixt the two, The Eng - lish Falls_ they

ev - 'ry cast. There was Mis - ter and Mis - sis Frost and son, A
the wa - ter-side, Where we rocked and pitched in the foam - ing - tide, As
thun - der squalls; A red - coat sen - try bid us stand, A
call Horse-shoe; Near Ta - ble Rock we all de - scend, Down

charm - ing la - dy of fif - ty - one, Whose vol - u - bil - i -
through the surge our boat did glide, But the snow kept drift - ing
broth of a boy from Pad - dy's land, With bay - o - net fixed and
wind - ing steps that nev - er end, The la - dies our aid we

ty   of   tongue,   Re - mind - ed   me   of   a   Chi - nese   gong.
o'er   the   track,   Which   made   our   trav - el - ling   rath - er   slack.
pen   in   hand   To   sign   our   names___   did   us   com - mand.
had   to   lend,   Each   beg-ging the   oth - er   her   pace   to   mend.

Refrain

Oh,   rum-bling, tum-bling, tear-ing a - way,   Wal - low-ing, bel-low - ing,   wet   with spray,   Like

Aunt   Deb-o - rah's   wash - ing day,   This   trip   to   Ni - ag - a - ra   Falls.___

The Logger's Boast

(Penobscot)

In free narrative style

1. Come all ye sons of free-dom, through-
2. When the white frost gilds the val-leys, the
3. The mu-sic of our bur-nished ax shall
4. When win-ter's snows are melt-ed and the

out the State of Maine; Come all ye gal-lant lum-ber-men and
cold con-geals the flood, When man-y men have naught to do to
make the woods re-sound, And man-y a loft-y pine— will—
ice-bound streams are free, We'll run our logs to mar-ket, then—

lis-ten to my strain: On the banks of the Pe-nob-scot, where the
earn their fam-'lies bread; When the swol-len streams are fro-zen, and the
tum-ble to the ground; At night ho! round our good camp-fire we will
haste our friends to see; How kind-ly true hearts wel-come us, our

Refrain

60

Inspired by Wolfe's victory over Montcalm on the Plains of Abraham high above the St. Lawrence River, this ballad purports to tell the story of the young British general's farewell to his beloved and of his death soon after he had been informed that Quebec was captured.

Brave Wolfe

(St. Lawrence)

Fervently and slowly

1. Cheer up your hearts, young men, let noth-ing fright you, Be not of a gal-lant mind, let that de-light you. Let not your cour-age fail, till af-ter tri-al, Nor let your fan-cy move at the first de-ni-al. 2. I

2. (I) went to see my love on-ly to woo her, I went to gain her love, not to un-do her. When e'er I spoke a word, my tongue did quiv-er, I could not speak my mind, while I was with her. 3. Love

3. (Love,) here's a dia-mond ring, long time I've kept it, 'Tis for your sake a lone that I have kept it, When you the pos-y read, think on the giv-er, Love, dam, re-mem-ber me, Or I'm un-done for-ev-er. 4. Brave

4. (Brave) Wolfe, then took his leave of his dear jew-el, Most sure-ly did she grieve, say-ing don't be cru-el, Said he, "'Tis for a space that I must leave you, Yet love, wher-e'er I go, I'll not for-get you." 8. (His)

5. So
6. (The)
7. (The)
8. (His)

then this gal - lant youth did — cross the — o - cean To free — A - mer -
drums did loud - ly — beat col - ors were fly - ing The pur - ple gore did —
French be - gan to — break their ranks and — fly - ing, Brave Wolfe be - gan to —
aid - de - camp re - plied, "'Tis — in our — fav - or, Que - bec with all her —

i - ca from her in - va - sion, He — land - ed at — Que -
stream and — men lay — dy - ing, When shot from off — his —
wake as he lay — dy - ing, He — lift - ed up — his —
pride, we — soon shall have her, She'll fall in - to — our

mp

bec with — all his par - ty, The cit - y to at -
horse, fell — this brave he - ro, And we la - ment his —
head while — guns did rat - tle, And to his ar - my —
hands with — all her treas - ure, "O, then," brave Wolfe re -

p

5.-6.-7.   8.

tack, both — brave and — heart - y. 6. The
loss in — weeds of — sor - row. 7. The
said "How — goes the — bat - tle?" 8. His
plied, "I — die with —   pleas - ure."

rit

Canadian Boat Song

(St. Lawrence)

Words by Thomas Moore
Old French Folk Tune

Thomas Moore wrote the words of this song to an air which the boatmen sang during a five-day trip down the St. Lawrence from Kingston to Montreal in 1804. The wind was so unfavorable the voyageurs found it necessary to row the entire distance.

Brightly

1. Faint - ly as tolls the ev' - ning chime, Our voic - es keep tune and our oars keep time, — Our voic - es keep tune and our oars keep time; Soon as the woods on shore look dim, We'll sing at St. Ann's our part - ing hymn;

2. Why should we yet our sail un - furl? There is not a breath the blue wave to curl, — There is not a breath the blue wave to curl; But when the wind blows off the shore, Oh! sweet - ly we'll rest the wear - y oar;

Row, broth-ers, row, the stream runs fast, The ra-pids are near and the
Blow, breez-es, blow, the stream runs fast, The ra-pids are near and the

p

day - light's past, The ra-pids are near and the day - light's past.
day - light's past, The ra-pids are near and the day - light's past.

ten.

rit.

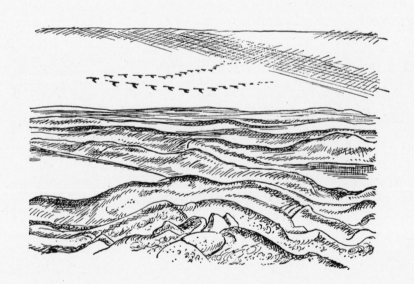

My Birchbark Canoe

(St. Lawrence)

French Folk Song
Translated by Marianne Lacroix

Dreamily and very slowly

1. Glid - ing in my birch ca - noe, Light - er than the danc - ing foam, I have met Saint Law - rence an - ger In
2. For my craft's white gleam - ing sides, All her seams so tight - ly sown, The birch gave me its smooth - est bark The
3. Where the rap - ids boil in thun - der, My ca - noe is my de - light. For if I must make a port - age Its
4. As the horse - man loves his steed, As the pil - grim loves his staff, I love my ca - noe and when I'm dead, O -

my   lit - tle   float - ing___   home, ___   Have
wood - land   roots   like   thongs have   grown, ___   With
weight   on   my   back   is___   slight, ___   A -
ver   turn   it,   on   my   be - half, ___   A -

met   and   braved___   it   and   come   through,   What —
pol - ished   pad - dles   now   she   rides___   Saint —
Turn   it   o - ver,   lie   in   un - der,   And —
bove   my   grave.___   That's   all   I   need   For   my

ev - er   rag - ing   storms   have   come.___
Law - rence   wa - ter   as   her   own.___
I've   a   cab - in   for   the   night.___
tomb - stone   and___   ep - i - taph.___

allarg.

Schuylkill Rowing Song

(1882)

Thomas Dunn English
W.T. Farlynne

Lively but not too fast

1. Clear and cloud-less is the night, The
2. Hark! the beat-ing oars keep time To

moon climbs up the dark blue sky, The winds have sunk to
mu - sic soft by fair lips sung, That like the sound of

mur - murs light, That o'er the wa - ters soft - ly sigh.
sweet bells chime, Rings out from voic - es clear and young.

Rip - pling wave - lets kiss the prow, of our light boat, that
Fad - ing lights a - long the shore, Now glance a mo - ment

safe - ly rides, As the stur - dy row - ers bow And
and are soft, Back from bridg - es arch - ing o'er, The

swift - ly through the stream she glides._____
mer - ry voic - es now are toss'd._____

Refrain

Com - rades row, light - ly row, Fast the time___ is

fly - ing; Com - rades row, light - ly row, The

The Ballad of Peter Gray

(Susquehanna, 1858)

Peter heard his love was lost, He knew not what to say,— He'd
Peter went away out West, To seek his for - ti - an,— But
Lucy heard of this bad news, A - bout poor Pet - er Gray,— She

half a mind to jump in - to, The Sus - que - han - i - a.
he was caught and scal - pi - ed, By a blood - y In - di - an.
wep' and wep' and wep - i - ed Her dear sweet life a - way.

Refrain

Blow ye winds of morn - ing, Blow ye winds heigh - o,

mf

4.-5.   6.

Blow ye winds of morn - ing, Blow,— blow,— blow.   5. Now blow.——
                                                    6. When
rall.   *mp*   *mf*

Old Butler's

(Susquehanna)

1. We swung a-round old But-ler's No dan-ger did we fear, Un-
2. There was a man up-on a raft His name it was Big Mose,—He

til we came to Saw-mill Rift and went plumb a-gainst the pier.—
hopped a-round a-mong the logs And— saved most all our clothes.—

Refrain (*more spirited and faster*)

And shove a-round the grog boys,—The cho-rus 'round the room.— For

we're the boys that fear no noise al— though we're far from home.—

As sung by Charles T. White and recorded by Helen Conlom

Such a Gettin' Upstairs

(Susquehanna)

Not fast

1. On a Sus-ke-han-nah raft I cum down de bay, An' I
2. I call on my gal Sal dat trades in sau-sag-es, An' dere
3. Say I "You see dat do'? Just mos-ey, mis-ter Joe" I'm a

danc'd an' I fro-lick'd, an I fid-dled all de way, Such a get-tin' up stairs I
I met big Joe, which make my dan-der riz, Such a get-tin' up stairs I
Sus-ke-han-nah boy, wot knows a ting or two, Such a get-tin' up stairs I

neb-ber did see, Such a get-tin' up stairs I neb-ber did see.
neb-ber did see, Such a get-tin' up stairs I neb-ber did see.
neb-ber did see, Such a get-tin' up stairs I neb-ber did see.

4. I ___ look him in de face un-til I make him grin An' den
5. And ___ den I show my sci-ence *Pre-nez,* *gar-dez* *vous,* Bung he
6. ___ Two be-hind, and two be-fore, Wait

I trow a back-a quid an' hit him on de shin, Such a get-tin' up__ stairs I
eye, break he shin, split he nose in two, Such a get-tin' up__ stairs I
'til you get to the jail house door, Such a get-tin' up__ stairs I

neb-ber did__ see, Such a get-tin' up__ stairs I neb-ber did__ see.
neb-ber did__ see, Such a get-tin' up__ stairs I neb-ber did__ see.
neb-ber did__ see, Such a get-tin' up__ stairs I neb-ber did__ see.

Songs of
the
Rivers of the South

THE MOVING yellow waters of southern streams excited the imaginations of the Negro slaves. The black people sang of the rivers and still do in songs that carry the strange magic with which they endow all their music.

The War Between the States, like many other wars, involved bitter struggles for the control of waterways and provided historic riverside incidents to be recorded in song.

Stephen Foster, planning that his "Old Folks at Home" should honor a southern stream, wrote "Way Down Upon the Pee Dee River" but was persuaded to change "the Pee Dee" to "the Swanee" for euphony's sake. Born in the valley of the Ohio, this greatest of all American song writers never lost his love for the rippling water highways, and made many of his works describe river life.

The Minstrel Shows of the mid-decades of the 19th Century were really elaborately costumed glee-choruses in blackface. They sang their way through a rigidly stylized program of dance songs, comic songs, and "songs of the heart," tenor solos with the rest of the group joining in the refrain. Many of the latter ballads were about beautiful young ladies, now dead, or at least forsaken, on the banks of a moonlit, southern river.

The crime song—folk-ballad narrative of an actual murder or other violent incident—has been more prevalent on the banks of southern streams than elsewhere but it may be found in all regions of the United States.

The Rose of Alabama

(Alabama, 1846)

Silas S. Steele

In robust rhythm, but not too fast

1. A — way from Mis - sis -
2. (I) land - ed on de
3. (Oh,) ar - ter d'reck - ley

sip - pi's vale, Wid' my ole hat dar for a sail, I
sand____ bank I sat up - on a hol - ler plank, An'
bye an' bye, De moon rose white as Ro - sey's eye, Den

cross'd up - on a cot - ton bale, To Rose of Al - a - ba - ma.
dare I made de ban - jo twank, For Rose of Al - a - ba - ma.
like a young coon out so sly, Stole Rose of Al - a - ba - ma.

Refrain

Oh, brown Ro - sey, De Rose ob Al - a - ba - ma, A

sweet to-bac-co po-sey, Is de Rose of Al-a-ba-ma, A

sweet to-bac-co po-sey Is de Rose of Al-a-ba-ma.
2. I
3. Oh,
ba-ma.
4. De
5. (I)
6. (And)

riv-er rolled, de crick-ets sing, De light-nin' bug he flash'd his wing, And
hug so long I can-not tell, For Ro-sey seemed to like it well, My
ev-'ry night in moon or show'r To hunt dat ban-jo for an hour, I

like a rope my arms I fling 'Round Rose of Al-a-ba-ma.
ban-jo in de riv-er fell, Oh Rose of Al-a-ba-ma.
meet my sweet to-bac-co flower, My Rose of Al-a-ba-ma.

78

Dearest Mae

(Catawba, 1847)

Words by Francis Lynch
Music by James Power

Slowly

1. Now dark-ies lis-ten to me, A story I'll re-late; It hap-pen'd in the val-ley in the old Car'-li-na state; Way down in de mead-ow 'twas dere I mow'd de hay, I al-ways work de hard-er when, I think of lub-ly Mae.

2. Old Mas-sa gib me holi-day, An' say he'd gib me more, I tank'd him be-ry kind-ly an' shoved my boat from shore; So down de riv-er I glides long, wid my heart so light and free, To de cot-tage ob my lub-ly Mae, I'd long'd so much to see.

3. On de banks of Ca-taw-ba, Whar de trees dey hang so low, De coon a-mong thar branch-es play, while de mink he keep be-low; Oh! dar is de spot an' Mae she look so neat, Her eyes dey spar-kle like de stars, her lips are red as beet.

legato
mp
mf
dim.
p

80

Refrain (*with expression*)

Oh, dear-est Mae, you're lub-ly as the day; Your eyes so bright, dey shine at night, When de moon am gone a-way.

Cumberland Gap

(Cumberland)

Very joyously

1. Cum-ber-land Gap is a no-ted place,
2. The first white man in Cum-ber-land Gap,

Three kinds of wa-ter to wash your face. Cum-ber-land Gap with its cliff and rocks
Was Doc-tor Walk-er, an Eng-lish chap. Dan-iel Boone on Pin-na-cle Rock,

Home of the pan-ther, skunk and bear and fox.
He killed In-di-ans with an old flint-lock.

marcato

Ol' Aunt Di-nah if you don't keer, Leave my lit-tle jug
Ol' Aunt Di-nah took a lit-tle spell, Broke my lit-tle jug

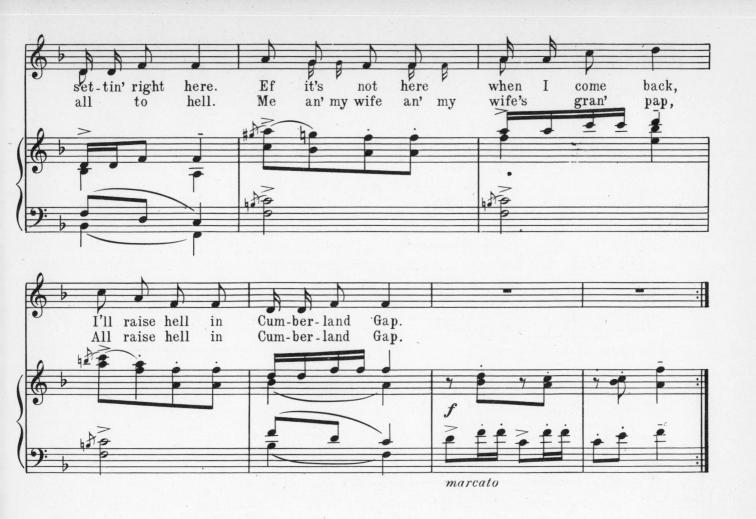

set-tin' right here. Ef it's not here when I come back,
all to hell. Me an' my wife an' my wife's gran' pap,

I'll raise hell in Cum-ber-land Gap.
All raise hell in Cum-ber-land Gap.

marcato

Poor Omie

(Deep)

The distinguished authority, B. L. Lunsford, states that "Jonathan Lewis drowned his sweetheart, Naomi Wise, in Deep River," North Carolina. This version is given as collected and sung by Frank Warner.

Simply, in a narrative fashion

1. Now, come on, you good peo-ple, and lis-ten while I tell The sto-ry of a girl called Le-o-ma Wise, _____ Her face was fair and hand-some, she was loved by ev-'ry one, But could not prove who caused her to die. _____
2. One sum-mer night he met her and took her for a ride, She thought that she was go-ing to be wed, _____ They came to old Deep Riv-er And so the sto-ry goes, "You've met your doom," these words the vil-lain said. _____
3. Next day they found her bod-y a-float-ing down the stream, And peo-ple for miles a-round did cry; _____ The vil-lain left the coun-try, they brought him back a-gain, But could not prove he caused her to die. _____
4. They say that on his death-bed, young John-son did con-fess That he had killed Le-o-ma Wise, _____ Now, come on, you good peo-ple, be-fore it is too late, You nev-er know just when you meet your doom.

84

Stonewall Jackson's Requiem
(James)

M. Deeves

Solemnly and slowly

1. The muf - fled drum is beat - ing, There's a sad and sol - emn tread; Our ban - ner's draped in mourn - ing, As it shrouds th' "il - lus - trious dead." Proud forms are bent with sor - row And all South - ern hearts are sore; The He - ro now is sleep - ing, No - ble Stone - wall is no

2. They've borne him to an hon - or'd grave, The lau - rel crowns his brow; By hal - lowed James's si - lent wave He's sweet - ly sleep - ing now. Vir - gin - ia to the South is dear, She holds a sac - red trust; Our fall - en braves from far and near Are cov - ered with her

more. Mid the rat-tling of the mus-kets And the can-non's thun-drous
dust; She_ shrines the spot where now is laid The brav-est of them

roar, He stained the field of glo-ry With his brave life's pre-cious
all, The mar-tyr of our coun-try's cause, Our i-dol-ized Stone-

gore; And though our flag waved proud-ly, We were vic-tors ere sun-
wall; But though his spir-it's waft-ed To the hap-py realms a-

set, The gal-lant deeds of Chance'-lors-ville Will min-gle with re-gret.
bove, His name shall live for-ev-er link'd With rev-er-ence and love.

'Twill Neber Do To Gib It Up So

(James, 1849)

With exuberant gaiety, but not too fast

1. I'm ole Mis-ter Brown, jist from de souf, I left Lynch-burg in de time ob de drowth; De
2. Ole Jim rib-ber I float-ed down, My back-er boat it run up-on de groun'; De

times dey got so bad in the place, Dat I neb-ber dare to show my face.
pine log come wid a rush-in' din, An' stove bote ends ob de ole boat in.

Refrain

'Twill neb-er do to gib it up so, 'Twill neb-er do to gib it up so, 'Twill

neb-er do to gib it up so, Mis-ter Brown, 'Twill neb-er do to gib it up so.

Darling Nelly Gray

(Kentucky, 1856)

B. R. Handy

1. There's a low green valley on the old Kentucky shore, There I've whiled many happy hours away, A sitting and a singing by the little cottage door, Where lived my darling Nelly
2. One night I went to see her, but "she's gone" the neighbors say, The white man bound her with his chain, They have taken her to Georgia for to wear her life away, As she toils in the cotton and the
3. My eyes are getting blinded, and I cannot see the way, Hark! there's somebody knocking at the door, Oh, I hear the angels calling and I see my Nelly Gray, Farewell to the old Kentucky

Gray._____ Oh, my poor Nel - ly Gray, they have
cane._____ Oh, my poor Nel - ly Gray, they have
shore._____ Oh, my dar - ling Nel - ly Gray, up in

tak - en you a - way, And I'll nev - er see my dar - ling an - y
tak - en you a - way, And I'll nev - er see my dar - ling an - y
heav - en there they say, That they'll nev - er take you from me an - y

more, I'm _ sit - ting by the riv - er and I'm
more, I'm _ sit - ting by the riv - er and I'm
more, I'm a - com - ing, com - ing, com - ing, as the

weep - ing all the day, For you've gone from the old Ken - tuck - y shore.__
weep - ing all the day, For you've gone from the old Ken - tuck - y shore.__
an - gels clear the way, Fare - well to the old Ken - tuck - y shore.__

Hunters of Kentucky

(Kentucky, 1822)

The author of the words of this song also wrote "The Old Oaken Bucket." Celebrating the successes of the Kentucky riflemen at the Battle of New Orleans, January 8, 1815, it was set to the music of an old folk song and first sung in America by the well-known tenor for whom it was written, Arthur Keene.

Tune: "Miss Bailey's Ghost"
Words by Samuel Woodworth

Bright and fresh

1. Ye gen-tle-men and la-dies fair, Who grace this fa-mous cit-y, Just lis-ten if you've time to spare, While I re-hearse a dit-ty; And for the op-por-

2. I s'pose you've read it in the prints, How Pack-en-ham at-tempt-ed To make old Hick'-ry Jack-son wince, But soon his scheme re-pent-ed; For we, with rif-les

3. But Jack-son he was wide a-wake, And was not scar'd at trif-les, For well he knew what aim we take With our Ken-tuck-y rif-les. So he led us down

4. They found, at last, 'twas vain to fight, Where lead was all the boot-y, And so they wise-ly took to flight, And left us all our beau-ty. And now, if dan-ger

tun - i - ty Con - ceive your - selves quite luck - y, For
read - y cock'd, Thought such oc - cas - ion luck - y, And
Cy - press swamp, The ground was low and muck - y, There
e'er an - noys, Re - mem - ber what our trade is, Just

'tis not oft - en that you see a hunt - er from Ken - tuck - y.
soon a - round the gen - 'ral flocked The hunt - ers of Ken - tuck - y.
stood John Bull in mar - tial pomp And there was old Ken - tuck - y.
send for us Ken - tuck - y boys, And we'll pro - tect you la - dies.

Refrain *(much slower)*
ten. ten.

Oh Ken - tuck - y, the hunt - ers of Ken - tuck - y! Oh Ken -

mf *rit*

tuck - y, the hunt - ers of Ken - tuck - y!

a tempo

My Old Kentucky Home

(Kentucky, 1852)

Stephen C. Foster

Slowly, with very deep feeling

1. The sun shines bright in the old Ken-tuck-y home, 'Tis
2. They hunt no more for the pos-som and the coon, On
3. The head must bow and the back will have to bend, Wher-

mp legato

sum - mer, the dark - ies are gay, The corn - top's ripe and the
mead - ow, the hill and the shore, They sing no more by the
ev - er the dark - y may go; A few more days and the

mead - ow's in bloom, While the birds make mu - sic all the
glim - mer of the moon, On the bench by the old cab - in
trou - ble all will end, In the field where sug - ar canes

day. The young folks roll on the lit - tle cab - in floor, All
door. The day goes by like a shad - ow o'er the heart, With
grow. A few more days for to tote the wea - ry load, No

merry, all hap-py and bright, By'n bye hard times comes a-
sor-row, where all was de-light, The time has come when the
mat-ter 'twill nev-er be bright, A few more days 'til we

knock-ing at the door, Then my old Ken-tuck-y home, good night.
dark-ies have to part, Then my old Ken-tuck-y home, good night.
tot-ter on the road, Then my old Ken-tuck-y home, good night.

Very tenderly

Weep no more, my la-dy, Oh, weep no more to-day! We will

sing one song for the old Ken-tuck-y home, For my old Ken-tuck-y home far a-way.

Betsy Baker

(Mississippi)

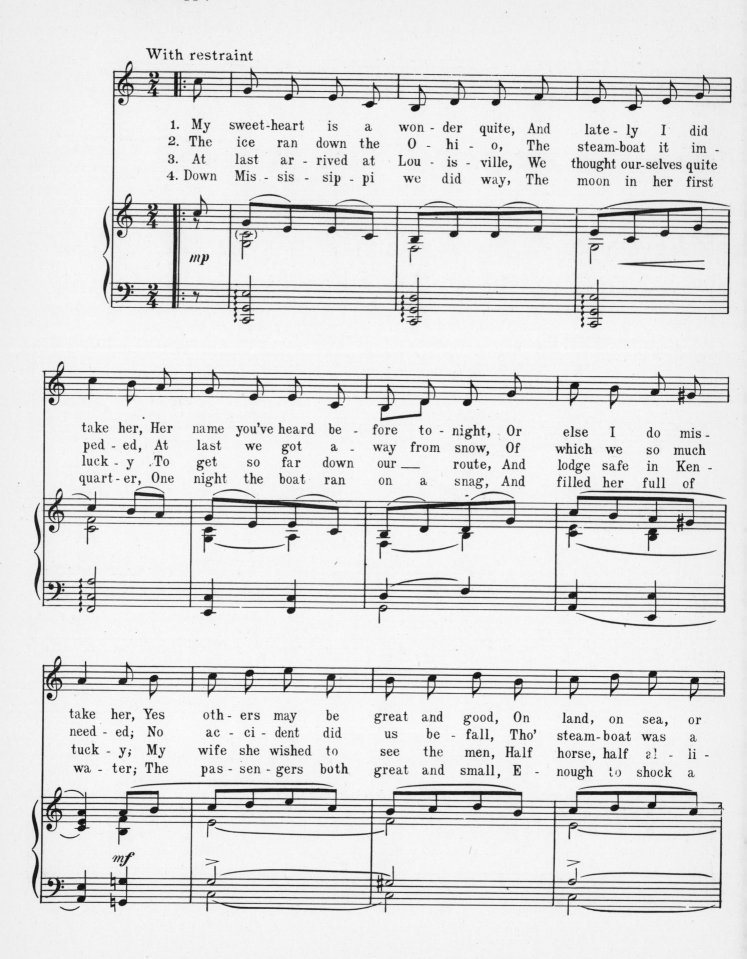

With restraint

1. My sweet-heart is a won-der quite, And late-ly I did take her, Her name you've heard be-fore to-night, Or else I do mis-take her, Yes oth-ers may be great and good, On land, on sea, or

2. The ice ran down the O - hi - o, The steam-boat it im-ped - ed, At last we got a - way from snow, Of which we so much need - ed; No ac-ci-dent did us be - fall, Tho' steam-boat was a

3. At last ar-rived at Lou - is - ville, We thought our-selves quite luck - y To get so far down our __ route, And lodge safe in Ken-tuck - y; My wife she wished to see the men, Half horse, half al - li -

4. Down Mis - sis - sip - pi we did way, The moon in her first quart - er, One night the boat ran on a snag, And filled her full of wa - ter; The pas - sen - gers both great and small, E - nough to shock a

lake_ sir, Few names have ev - er fair - er stood Than
shak - er, I was not then blown up at all, Ex -
gat_ or, I fear - ful was that they might gouge My
Quak_ er, Had scarce - ly an - y clothes at all. What a

my sweet Bet - sy Bak - er, Few names have ev - er
cept by Bet - sy Bak - er, I was not then blown
love - ly Bet - sy Bak - er, I fear - ful was that
sight for Bet - sy Bak - er, Had scarce - ly an - y

fair - er stood Than my sweet Bet - sy Bak - er.
up at all, Ex - cept by Bet - sy Bak - er.
they might gouge My love - ly Bet - sy Bak - er.
clothes at all, What a sight for Bet - sy Bak - er.

A Life on the Vicksburg Bluff

(Mississippi)

With words of jocose complaint set to the stirring tune of "A Life on the Ocean Wave," the besieged Confederate soldiers made light of their hardships during Grant's seige of Vicksburg.

A. Dalsheimer
Tune "A Life On The Ocean Wave"

Lustily

1. A life on the Vicks burg bluff, A home in the trench - es deep, Where we dodge Yank shells e - nough, And our old pea - bread won't keep, On old Lo - gan's beef I pine, For there's

2. Old Grant is starv-ing us out, Our grub is wast-ing a - way, Pemb don't know what he's a - bout, And he has-n't for man-y a day. So we'll bur - y old Lo - gan to - night, From

3. Tex-as steers are no long-er in view, Mule steaks are now "done up brown," While pea bread, mule roast and mule stew, Are our fare in Vicks - burg town. And the song of our heart shall be, While the

96

fat on his bones no more;___ Oh! give me some pork and
tough beef we'll be set free;___ We'll put him far out of
Yanks and their gun - boats rave;___ A life in a bomb - proof for

brine,___ ___ And truck from a sut - ler's store.___
sight,___ ___ No more of his meat for me.___
me,___ ___ And a tear on old Lo - gan's grave.___

Refrain

A life on the Vicks - burg bluff,___ A___ home in the trench - es

deep.___ Where we dodge Yank shells e - nough___ And our

old pea-bread won't keep, _____ Pea-bread, _____ pea-

mp

bread, _____ Our old pea-bread won't keep; _____ Pea-

bread, _____ pea-bread, _____ Our old pea-bread won't keep: _____

Nelly Was a Lady

(Mississippi, 1849)

Stephen C. Foster

Very broad

1. Down on the Mis-sis-sip-pi float-ing,
2. Now I'm un-hap-py an' I'm weep-ing,
3. When I saw my Nel-ly in de morn-ing,

Long time I trab-ble on de way,
Can't tote de cot-ton wood no more,
Smile till she o-pen'd up her eyes,

All night de cot-ton wood a-
Last night while Nel-ly was a-
Seem'd like de light ob day a-

tot-ing,
sleep-ing,
dawn-ing,

Sing for my true lub all de day.
Death came a-knock-in' at de door.
Just 'fore de sun be-gin to rise.

Refrain

Nel-ly was a la-dy, Last night she died; Toll de bell for lub-ly Nell, My

dark Vir - gin - ny bride. Nel - ly was a la - dy, Last night she died,

Toll de bell for lub - ly Nell, My dark Vir - gin - ny bride.

My Old Cabin Home

(Mississippi, 1858)

Moderately

mp legato

1. I am go-ing far a - way, Far a-
2. I am go-ing to leave this land, With

way to leave you now, To the Mis - sis - sip - pi val - ley I am
this, our dark - y band,____ To trav - el all the wide____ world____

go - ing; I will take my old ban - jo, And I'll
o - ver; And____ when I get tired I will

sing this lit - tle song, A - way down in my Old Cab - in Home.
set - tle down to rest, A - way down in my Old Cab - in Home.

mf

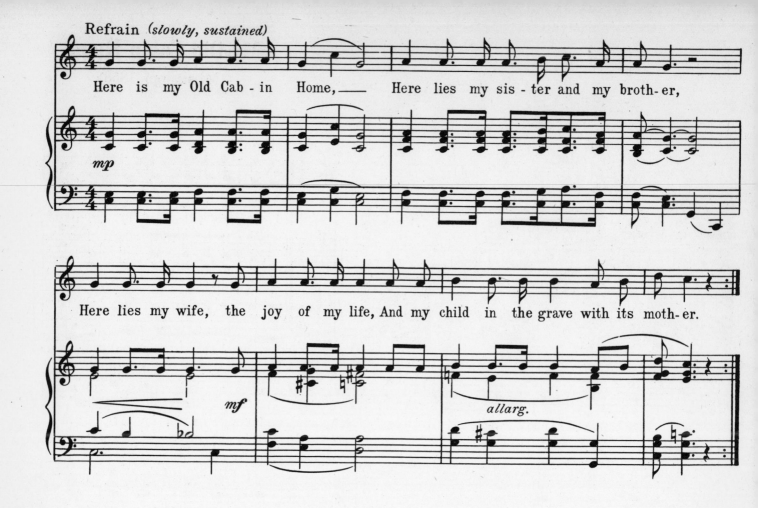

Refrain (*slowly, sustained*)

Here is my Old Cab-in Home,____ Here lies my sis-ter and my broth-er,

Here lies my wife, the joy of my life, And my child in the grave with its moth-er.

Roll Out! Heave Dat Cotton

(Mississippi, 1877)

Will S. Hays

Gaily and rhythmically

1. I hear dat bell a - ring - ing, I see de Cap - tain stand, Boat done blow'd her whis - tle, I know she's gwine to land. I hear de mate a call - in', "Go git out the plank, Rush out wid de head - line, An' tie her to de bank."

2. It's ear - ly in de morn - ing, Be - fore we see de sun, "Roll a - board dat cot - ton, An' get back in a run." De Cap - tain's in a hur - ry, I know what he means, Wants to beat de Sher - lock, Down to New Or - leans.

3. I hear dat mate a - shout - ing, An' see him on de shore, "Hur - ry boys! be live - ly, Ain't but fif - ty more." We ain't got time to tar - ry, Here at dis cot - ton pile, We gwine to git an - nod - der, Be - low here for - ty mile.

Refrain

Roll out! __ heave dat cot-ton __ Roll out! __ heave dat cot-ton __
Roll out! __ heave dat cot-ton, ain't got long to stay. __

Way Down in Cairo

(Mississippi, 1850)

Stephen C. Foster

Moderately lively

1. Oh, la - dies—— don't you blush, when
2. Some - times de nig-gah's life is sad, some
3. Now we lib on de fat—— land, Now

mp

I come out to play, I on-ly mean to please you all and den I'se gwine a-way.
times his life is gay, —— When de work don't come too hard, he's sing-ing all de day.
we lib on de lean, —— When we hab no cake to bake, we sweep de kitch-en clean.

Refrain

I hear my true lub weep, I hear my true lub sigh;

Way down in Ca - i - ro dis nig - ga's gwine to die.

poco rit.

Poor Juna

(Pearl, 1856)

Miss Armstrong

With tranquillity

1. Pearl riv-er-side is far a-way In the old Mis-sis-sip-pi State, And our old cab-in stands a-lone, With Ju-na at the gate. I told her I must go a-way That I

2. Oh Ju-na was a sim-ple child, Had pret-ty shin-ing curls And the white folks loved her best of all The young mu-lat-to girls; 'Twas wrong of me to leave her so, In the

3. If you should ev-er trav-el to the South In the old Mis-sis-sip-pi State, Don't fail to find the cab-in out, With Ju-na at the gate. Tell her to wait a lit-tle while, Tell

106

should not be out late, And Ju - na stands with tear - ful
old Mis - sis - sip - pi State; And I must quick - ly hur - ry
her in hopes to wait; Tell her that I will break the

eye, To meet me at the gate.
home, To take poor Ju - na from the gate.
chains, That bind her to the gate.

Refrain

Our old cab - in stands up - on the stream In the old Mis - sis - sip - pi

State, And I must quick - ly hur - ry home, To take poor Ju - na from the gate.

Ole Pee Dee

Gaily

1. In Souf Car-li-na I was born, I chop de wood an' husk de corn, De roast-in' ear to de house I bring, De nig-ger cotch me an' I sing;
2. They took me out on tat-er hill, They make me dance a-gainst my will, I dance all round de tat-er hole, De nig-gers punch me wid a pole. } Ring de hoop! blow de horn! Cotch de nig-ger a-steal-in' corn, Way down in de low groun' fiel', three four mile from Pom-pey's heel.
3. Down de rib-ber I spied a ship, I slid down on my un-der lip, Den hop on board an' cross de drink, It make de nig-gers' giz-zard wink.

From *Slave Songs of the Georgia Sea Islands*, copyright, 1942, by Lydia Parrish, and reprinted by her permission, and the permission of Creative Age Press, Inc., New York.

On the Banks of the Old Pee Dee

Slowly, in a contemplative mood

1. My love and I we took a
2. He took her by the lil-y-white

walk On the banks of the old Pee-dee, And as we walked we gent-ly
hand, And swung her 'round and 'round, Then threw her in-to the wa-ters

talked When our wed-ding day would be."On-ly say, on-ly say, that you will be mine, And your
deep, And there he watched her drown."Be-cause she said she'd nev-er be mine, And her

home will ev-er be, Where the si-lent wa-ters flow On the banks of the old Pee-dee."
home would nev-er be, Where the si-lent wa-ters flow On the banks of the old Pee-dee."

Way Down on the Ole Pee Dee

Moderately fast and resolutely

Way down on the ole Pee - dee, Way down on the ole Pee -

dee, Sum - mer night the moon - shine bright

Sal - ly you can see. I wish that gal was

mine, I wish that gal was mine,

"All Quiet along the Potomac"

(1863)

The authorship of this song is in doubt, Major Lamar Fontaine, 2nd Virginia Cavalry, and Mrs. Ethel Lyn Beers being the leading claimants. The tune too is a subject of controversy; it has been credited to Henry Coyle, leader, and also to J. Dayton, member, of the First Connecticut Artillery Band.

1. "All qui-et a-long the Po-to-mac" they say, Ex-cept now and then a stray pick-et Is shot as he walks on his beat, to and fro, By a ri-fle-man hid in the thick - -
2. "All qui-et a-long the Po-to-mac" to-night, Where the sol-diers lie peace-ful-ly dream-ing, Their tents, in the rays of the clear au-tumn moon, Or the light of the watch-fires are gleam - -

et. 'Tis noth - ing a pri - vate or two, now and
ing. A trem - u - lous sigh, as the gen - tle night

then, Will not count in the news of the bat - tle;
wind Through the for - est leaves soft - ly is creep - ing:

Not an of - fi - cer lost, on - ly one of the
While stars up a - bove, with their glit - ter - ing

men, Moan - ing out all a - lone the death rat - tle.
eyes, Keep guard, for the ar - my is sleep - ing.

113

Grave of Washington

(Potomac, 1846)

Marshall S. Pike

1. Dis - turb not his slum - bers, let Wash - ing - ton sleep, 'Neath the boughs of the wil - low that o - ver him weep; His arm is un - nerved, but his deeds re - main bright, As the stars in the dark vault - ed heav - en at night. Oh! wake not the he - ro, his

2. A - wake not his slum - bers, tread light - ly a - round, 'Tis the grave of a free - man, 'tis Lib - er - ty's mound; Thy name is im - mor - tal, our free - dom you won, Brave sire of Co - lum - bia, our own Wash - ing - ton. Oh! wake not the he - ro, his

battles are o'er, Let him rest un - dis - turbed on Po -
battles are o'er, Let him rest, calm - ly rest, on his

to - mac's fair shore; On the riv - er's green bor - der so
dear na - tive shore; While the stars and the stripes of our

flow - er - y drest, With the hearts he loved fond - ly, let
coun - try shall wave, O'er the land that can boast of a

Wash - ing - ton rest, With the hearts he loved fond - ly, let Wash - ing - ton rest.
Wash - ing - ton's grave, O'er the land that can boast of a Wash - ing - ton's grave.

allargando

Baby, Did You Hear?

(St. Johns)

With sincere feeling and slowly

1. Ba - by did you hear___ All your men goin' to leave you,
2. Ba - by did you hear___ All your fur - ni - ture goin' to leave you,
3. Ba - by did you hear___ Me and my sweet - ie's goin' a - way,

Yes, Lord, on the next pay day?
Yes, Lord, on the next pay day?
Yes, Lord, on the next pay day?

Refrain

Ba - by, did you hear___ Me and my sweet - ie's goin' to ride the Cher - o -

kee up the Saint John Riv - er, And nar - y a cent will I be the giv - er.

In 1884, at the age of 23, Delius lived on the old Spanish Solano Grove overlooking the St. Johns River. This song, part of his symphonic poem "Appalachia," is an old slave song which he collected at that time.

Oh Honey, I'm Going Down the River
(St. Johns)

Very slowly, with much expression

Oh, hon-ey, I am go-ing down the riv-er in the morn-ing, Heigh-ho, heigh-ho, down the might-y riv-er; Oh, hon-ey, I'll be gone when next the whip-poor-will's a-call-ing, And don't you be too lone-some, love, and don't you fret and cry; For the dawn will soon be break-ing,— The ra-diant moon— is nigh,— And you'll

find me ev-er a-wait-ing, Heigh ho,_ heigh ho, heigh ho, heigh ho, And you'll

find me ev-er a-wait-ing, My own sweet Nel-ly Gray. La-la-

la-la-la, la-la-la-la-la,_ la-la-la- la-la-la-la-la-la-la, La-la-

la-la-la, la-la-la-la-la,_ La-la-la-la-la,_ T'ords the morn-ing lift a voice, let the

scent-ed woods re-joice and ech-oes swell a-cross the might-y stream._

The Vance Song

(Sandy)

Sorrowfully, but not too slowly

mp

1. Green are the woods where San - dy flows, Peace it dwell - eth there, Se - cure the— red buck roams the wood, In the val - ley lies the bear.—
2. San - dy no more will Vance be - hold, Nor drink of its crys - tal wave, The par - tial— judge pro - nounced his doom, The— hunt - er found his death.—
3. I killed the man I don't de - ny, He said that he would kill me first, And for this I am con - demned to die, The— jur - y have all a - greed.—
4. Fare - well my friends and chil - dren dear, To you I will bid fare - well; And when I— reach fair Ca - naan's shore I— hope to meet with you.—

rit

Gentle Nettie Moore

(Santee, 1857)

G. S. Pike

With languid sentiment

1. In a lit - tle white cot - tage, Where the
2. Be - low us in the val - ley, On the

trees are ev - er green, And the climb - ing ros - es blos - som by the
San - tee's danc - ing tide, Of a sum - mer eve I'd launch my o - pen

door. I've_ oft - en sat and lis - ten'd to the mu - sic of the birds, And the
boat; And_ when the moon was ris - ing, and the stars be - gan to shine, Down the

gen - tle voice of charm - ing Net - tie Moore.
riv - er we so mer - ri - ly would float.

Refrain

Oh! I miss you, Net-tie Moore, And my hap-pi-ness is o'er, While a

spir-it sad a-round my heart has come; And the bus-y days are long, And the

nights are lone-ly now, For you're gone from our lit-tle cot-tage home.

poco rit

"Stonewall Jackson's Way"

(Shenandoah)

These words were found in the pocket of a soldier of the Stonewall Brigade who fell during the bitter fighting in the Shenandoah Valley. Their author is thought to be J. W. Palmer.

Words by J. W. Palmer.

In a military spirit

1. Come, stack arms, men — pile on the rails, Stir up the camp-fire bright; No mat-ter if — the can-teen fails, We'll make a roar-ing night; Here Shen-an-do-ah crawls a-long, Here

2. We see him now — the old slouched hat Couched o'er his eye as-kew; The shrewd, dry smile — the speech so pat, So calm, so blunt, so true; "Blue Light El-der" knows 'em well: Says

3. He's in the sad-dle now! Fall in! Stead-y the whole bri-gade! Hill's at the ford, — cut off; we'll win His way out, ball and blade. What mat-ter if our shoes are worn? What

f marcato

burly Blue - Ridge ech-oes strong, To swell the bri-gade's
he "That's Bank's,— he's fond of shell; Lord, save his soul! we'll
mat-ter if__ our feet are torn? Quick step! we're with him

rous - ing - song, Of "Stone - wall Jack - son's way."__
give him well" That's "Stone - wall Jack - son's way."__
ere the dawn! That's "Stone - wall Jack - son's way."__

Stone River

Stone River is a tributary of the Cumberland River. It rises in the mountains of north-eastern Tennessee and flows in a northwesterly course to join the Cumberland not far from Nashville.

Calmly

1. A - mong the pines that
2.(As) night closed down the

o - ver - look Stone Riv - er's rock - y bed, O -
blood - y __ scenes, Re - turn - ing o'er the dead, I

hi - o mourns a - man - y a son that's num - bered with the dead. 2. As
heard the pit - i - ful mourns of one laid low by mor - tal

wounds. 4.(They) sent me down to ask of __ him If
3. I fill'd his can - teen from a __ spring Be -

low Stone Riv - er's banks; I built a fire of
he did wish to send Some last re - quest of

ced - ar wood, The night be - ing cold and damp. 4. They
part - ing words To a moth - er, sis - ter or friend.

3. 4.

mf

Old Folks at Home

(Suwannee, 1851)

Stephen C. Foster

Very slowly with great warmth

1. Way down up-on the Swa-nee rib-ber, Far far a-way;
2. All round de lit-tle farm I wan-dered, When I was young;
3. One lit-tle hut a-mong de bush-es, One dat I love;

Dere's wha' my heart is turn-ing eb-ber, Dere's wha' de old folks stay.
Den man-y hap-py days I squan-dered, Man-y de songs I sung.
Still sad-ly to my mem-'ry rush-es, No mat-ter where I rove.

All up and down de whole cre-a-tion, Sad-ly I roam;
When I was play-ing wid my brud-der, Hap-py was I,
When will I see de bees a hum-ming, All round de comb;

Still long-ing for de old plan-ta-tion, And for de old folks at home.
Oh, take me to my kind old mud-der, Dere let me live and die.
When will I hear de ban-jo strum-ming, Down in my good old home?

All de world am sad and drear-y; Eb-'ry-where I roam,

Oh, dark-ies how my heart grows wear-y, Far from de old folks at home.

Ole Tare River

(Tar)

Apparently the Old Tare River of this song and the Old Tar River which is celebrated in the song that follows are identical. North Carolina's Tar River probably inspired them both.

Rhythmically, but not fast

1. Way__ down in North Car' - lin - a
2. De ole watch - dog smelt all a - round
3. Now Miss Di - nah I'm goin to leave you

On de banks of Ole Tare Riv - er,
He found de coon jest lef de ground
And when I'm gone don't let it grieve you

I go from dar to A - la - ba - ma
Den he bark right up de tree__
First to the win - dow den to de do'

For to see my ole Aunt Han - nah.
De ole coon says you can't ketch me.
Look - ing for to see de ban - jo.

Ole Tar River

Oh, on the ole Tar Riv-er, O — ee! Oh, on the ole Tar Riv-er, Lord,— Lord, the ole Tar Riv-er!— Tar Riv-er goin' run to-mor-row O— — ee!— Tar Riv-er goin' run to-mor-row Lord,— Lord, the ole Tar Riv-er!— Tar Riv-er run black an' dir-ty, O- ee!— Tar Riv-er run black an'

dir - ty,   Lord,___ Lord, the ole Tar Riv - er!___ Ole Tar Riv - er run free an'

eas - y, O___ ee! Ole Tar Riv - er run free an' eas - y, Lord,___

___ Lord, the ole Tar Riv - er___   Way down, way down,   in the coun - try,

Way down, way down,   in the coun - try Lord,_ Lord, the ole Tar Riv - er.___

Ellie Rhee

(Tennessee, mid 19th Century)

Septimus Winner

Longingly

1. Sweet El-lie Rhee, so dear to me, Is lost for-ev-er—more; Our home was down in Ten-nes-see, Be-fore dis cru-el—war.

2. Oh, why did I from day to day Keep wish-ing to be—free, And from my mas-sa run a-way, And leave my El-lie— Rhee.

Refrain

mf espressivo

Then car-ry me back to Ten-nes-see, Back where I long to be; A-mong the fields of yel-low corn, To my dar-ling El-lie— Rhee.

On that Hill by the Tennessee

(1891)

Maj. Alfred R. Calhoun, U. S. V.
Horatio C. King, U. S. V.

Solemnly, but not too slowly

1. I am get-ting bowed, and I've long_ been_ gray,
2. A_ bu-gler in gray came down_ to the shore, And
3. There un-der that oak, we_ made them one_ grave Your

Vet -'ran from the South - ern land, But a wave from the past fills my
sig - nalled truce to the blue, And two cap - tains rode out 'mid the
eyes and mine, friend, were damp, As we cut in the bark; They were

heart to - day, At the touch of your_ strong brown hand, Man-y years have-
ruck and gore, I was one_ the_ oth - er was you. We met 'neath a
foe - men brave, Then each turn'd_ and_ rode back to camp, Like true men we_

passed, Since you and I have met, Though it seems but a
tree Where two young sol - diers lay, We shout - ed, but they
fought Un-til fight - ing was vain, For those who drew

day to me; When we bur-ied our dead with the
gave no sign; The one was my broth-er, who'd
sword on your side; But I've pray'd through man-y years To

bat-tle dew wet on that hill by the Ten-nes-see.
fall-en in the fray, The oth-er was broth-er of thine.
meet you a-gain, For the sake of the broth-er who died.

Refrain

But a truce, a truce that shall nev-er be broke, Has come for you and me, We are

broth-ers at heart through the broth-ers who fell On that hill by the Ten-nes-see.

Uncle Ned

(Tennessee, 1848)

Stephen C. Foster

In a smooth, narrative mood

1. Dar_ was an' old nig-ger an' dey call'd him Un-cle Ned, But he's dead long, long a-go, He had no wool on de for' of his head, On de place where de wool ought to grow.

2. (Un-cle) Ned he was mar-ried when he was ber-ry young, To a yal-ler gal dey call Lu-cy Lee, She died in tree week, by an' al-li-ga-tor's tongue, On de banks ob de old Ten-nes-see.

3. (Un-cle) Ned he shed tears but he could-n't bring her to, So he bu-ry her, den look for an-od-er, De gals lub him so, dat dey all round him flew, An' poor old Ned near-ly smod-er.

Refrain (not fast)

Den lay down de shub-ble_ and de hoe, Hang up de fid-dle and de bow, Dar's

no more work for Un-cle Ned, He's gone where de good nig-gers go. 2. Un-cle
3. Un-cle

go. 4. Un-cle Ned he had fin-gers as long as de corn brake, Do' he
5.(Un-cle) Ned when he die Mis-sy look ber-ry bad, And de

had no eyes for to see, And he had no teeth for to
tears dey run down like de rain, And Mis-sy turn pale, for she

eat de corn cake So he forc'd to let de corn-cake be.
feel ber-ry sad, Cas she neb-ber see old Ned a-gain.

Refrain

Den lay down de shub - ble and de hoe, Hang up de fid-dle and de bow, Dar's

no more work for Un - cle Ned, He's gone where de good nig-gers go. 5. Un-cle go.

Tom-big-bee River

S. S. Steele

Quietly

1. On Tom-big-bee riv-er so
2. All the day in the field the soft
3. With my hands on the ban-jo and
4. One night the stream bore us

bright I was born, In a hut made of husks of the tall yel-low
cot-ton I hoe, I think of my Ju-la and sing, as I
toe on the oar, I sing to the sound of the riv-er's soft
so far a-way, That we could-n't come back so we thought we'd just

corn; And there I first met with my Ju-la so
go. Oh, I catch her a bird with a wing of true
roar. While the stars they look down at my Ju-la so
stay. Oh, we spied a tall ship with a flag of true

true, And I rowed her a - bout in my Gum tree ca - noe.
blue, And at night sail her round in my Gum tree ca - noe.
true, And dance in her eye in my Gum tree ca - noe.
blue, And it took us in tow with my Gum tree ca - noe.

ten.

a tempo

Refrain (*smoothly*)

Sing - ing row a - way, row, O'er the wa - ters so blue, Like a

mf

feath - er we'll float in my Gum tree ca - noe.

poco rit

Songs of
the
Rivers of the West

SONGS of transportation multiplied rapidly as the early Americans moved toward the Mississippi. The melodies that set a slow beat to the work at the raft-sweeps gave way to the livelier rowing tunes of the keelboatmen. Then came the sophisticated and genteel ditties of the gingerbreaded steamboat era.

While the boat songs rang across the river waters, pioneers sang of Indian fights and buffalo hunts and mustang hooves pounded out the rhythm of cowboy lullabies to herds of cattle on the vast prairies. Long drives to market were punctuated by all too infrequent rivers where the lowing cows could slake their thirst. A river was something to sing about at summer's end on the parched plains.

The finding of gold on the banks of the Sacramento inspired many songs of eager dreamers yearning for the precious river sands of the West. Some of them were adapted by sailors into sea chanties that livened the long voyage around the Horn.

The western gold-towns, growing with incredible speed, disappearing as suddenly, fostered the teary sentimental balladry of the womanless frontier.

The Bank of the Arkansaw

Very brightly

1. I start-ed out with Maw and Paw,
2. Two lit-tle In-dians and one old squaw
3. Pret-ti - est lit-tle girl I ev - er saw

Down on the bank of the Ar - kan - saw; Plowed the crop with a
Set - tin' on the bank of the Ar - kan - saw; Nev - er put out a
Lived on the bank of the Ar - kan - saw; Eyes were blue and her

mang - y plug, Sold the corn in a gal - lon jug.
hook and line, Steal __ all the big fish of mine.
cheeks were red, She __ was sweet as gin - ger - bread.

Refrain

Corn - stalk fid - dle and a shoe - string bow, "Rare back, Da - vy's

all I know. Had-n't a-been for cot-ton eyed Joe,

I'd a-been mar-ried a long time a-go.

Voyageur's Song

(Chicago)

French Canadian Folk Tune

In steady, sprightly rhythm

1. Joy to-thee, my brave ca-noe,—
2. Gent-ly, now, my brave ca-noe,—

There's no wing so swift as you; Right and left the bub-bles rise—
Keep your foot-ing sure and true, For the rap-id close be-neath,—

Right and left the pine wood flies; Birds and clouds and
Leaps and shouts his song of death; Now one plunge and

tide and— wind, We shall leave ye all be-hind.
all is— done, Now one plunge, the all goal is— won.

Refrain

Joy to thee, my brave ca-noe,— There's no wing so swift as you,

Joy to thee, my brave ca-noe,— There's no wing so swift as you.

Illinois

(1869)

Words by C. H. Chamberlain
Music by Archibald Johnston

With tranquility

1. By thy riv-ers gent-ly flow-ing, Il-li-nois, Il-li-nois, O'er thy prai-ries ver-dant grow-ing, Il-li-nois, Il-li-nois, Comes an ech-o on the breeze, Rus-tling thro' the leaf-y trees, And its mel-low tones are these,— Il-li-nois, Il-li-nois, And its

2. (From a) wil-der-ness of prai-ries, Il-li-nois, Il-li-nois, Straight thy way and nev-er va-ries, Il-li-nois, Il-li-nois, Till up-on the in-land sea Stands Chi-ca-go, great and free, Turn-ing all the world to thee,— Il-li-nois, Il-li-nois, Turn-ing

3. (When you) heard your coun-try call-ing, Il-li-nois, Il-li-nois, Where the shot and shell were fall-ing, Il-li-nois, Il-li-nois, When the South-ern host with-drew, Pit-ting Gray a-gainst the Blue, There were none more brave than you,— Il-li-nois, Il-li-nois, There were

mel - low tones are these, __ Il - li - nois! 2. From a
all the world to thee, __ Il - li - nois! 3. When you
none more brave than you, __ Il - li - nois!

4. Not with - out thy won - drous sto - ry, Il - li - nois, Il - li - nois, Can be
5. (When the) Cu - bans struck for free - dom, Il - li - nois, Il - li - nois, Un - cle
6. (Some en) - camped at Chick - a - mau - ga, Il - li - nois, Il - li - nois, Oth - ers

writ the na - tion's glor - y, Il - li - nois, Il - li - nois; On the
Sam re - solved to aid them, Il - li - nois, Il - li - nois; And for
fell at San - ti - a - go, Il - li - nois, Il - li - nois; Oth - ers

rec - ord of thy years, A - bra'm Lin - coln's name ap - pears, Grant and
men on land and sea, Il - li - nois said: Call on me! For the
anx - ious for a call, They will march, or fight or fall, They are

146

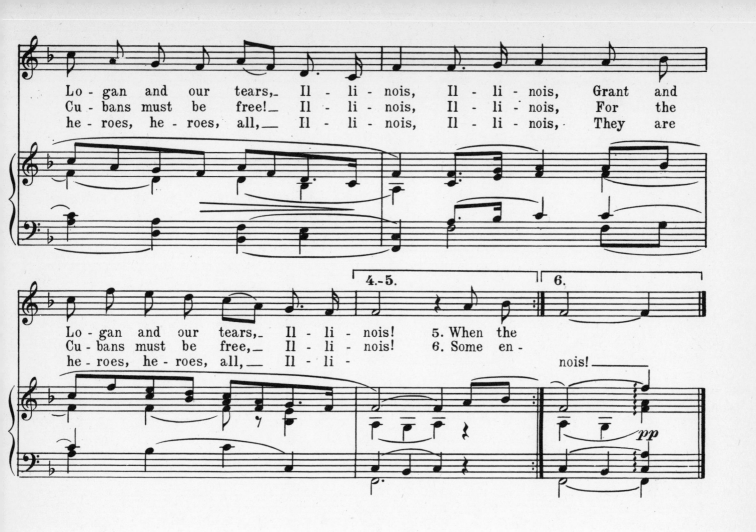

Lo - gan and our tears,_ Il - li - nois, Il - li - nois, Grant and
Cu - bans must be free!_ Il - li - nois, Il - li - nois, For the
he - roes, he - roes, all,_ Il - li - nois, Il - li - nois, They are

4.-5. ‖ **6.**

Lo - gan and our tears,_ Il - li - nois! 5. When the
Cu - bans must be free,_ Il - li - nois! 6. Some en -
he - roes, he - roes, all,_ Il - li - nois!_

Song of the Kansas Emigrants

(Kansas, 1875)

John G. Whittier
(Air: Auld Lang Syne)

Slowly, with almost religious feeling

1. We cross the prai - rie as of old Our fa - thers crossed the sea, To make the West as they the East The home - stead of the free. We go to rear a wall of men On Free - dom's South - ern line, And plant be - side the cot - ton tree The rug - ged north - ern pine.

2. (We're) flow - ing from our na - tive hills As our free riv - ers flow; The bless - ing of our Moth - er - land Is on us as we go. We go to plant her com - mon schools On dis - tant prai - rie swells, And give the Sab - baths of the wild The mu - sic of her bells.

3. (Up) - bear - ing like the Ark of old The Bi - ble in our van, We go to test the truth of God A - gainst the fraud of man. No pause nor rest, save where the streams That feed the Kan - sas run, Save where our pil - grim gon - fa - lon Shall flout the set - ting sun.

p *molto legato* *mf* *dimin.* *mf*

1.-2. 3.

148

The Rebel's Escape

(Licking, post Civil War)

In a narrative mood

This song appears here as sung to the editor by an elderly white supercargo at midnight on the steamboat docks at Memphis. Another version appears in *Devil's Ditties*, by Jean Thomas under the title "War Song."

1. Come all you jol-ly sol-diers, I will sing to you a song; I'll try to be brief, I will not de-tain you long, Con-cern-ing all my troub-les and how they did ad-vance, And how I got a-round them and what a nar-row chance.

2. With a bot-tle of good whis-ky I put the guard to sleep; Then down up-on my knees so sly-ly I did creep, And when I had gone a-round them and sly-ly I did creep, found I had got through, I set down up-on a lit-tle rock and there put on my shoe.

3. The fer-ry boat was guard-ed and I had na-ry horse; I cast my eyes a-round, a lit-tle raft I spied, I thought by good judg-ment I could get to the oth-er side; I jumped up-on my lit-tle raft, and gent-ly sailed a-cross.

4. Not thank-ing them for fer-ry-ing nor oth-er-wise a horse, I struck out up the Lick-ing I set my course for home To see my wife and chil-dren, for that was my in-tent, To see my wife and chil-dren that I had left at home.

To the West

(Missouri, mid 19th Century)

C. M.
H. R.

In a robust and spirited tempo

1. To the West! To the West! To the land ___ of the free, Where might-y Mis - sou - ri rolls down to the sea. Where a man is a man, if he's will - ing to toil, And the humb - lest may gath - er the

2. To the West! To the West! Where the riv - ers that flow, Run thou - sands of miles, spread - ing out as they go. Where the green wav - ing for - ests shall e - cho our call, As wide as all Eng - land and

fruit of the soil. Where chil-dren are bless-ings, and
free to us all. Where the prai-ries like seas where the

he who hath most, Has aid for his for-tune and rich-es to
bil-lows have roll'd, Are broad as the king-doms and em-pires of

boast. Where the young may ex-ult, and the a-ged may
old. And the lakes are like o-ceans in storm or in

rest, A-way, far a-way, to the land of the west.
rest, A-way, far a-way, to the land of the west.

poco rit.

To the West! To the West! To the land ___ of the free, Where mighty Mis - sou - ri rolls down to the sea. Where the young may ex - ult and the a - ged may rest, A - way, far a - way! To the land of the west!

The Wide Missouri

Sustained, slow tempo

1. Oh Shan - na - dore, I
2. (For) sev'n long years I
3. (She) would not have me

love your daugh - ter, Hi - oh, The roll - ing riv - er! — I'll
court - ed Nan - cy, Hi - oh, The roll - ing riv - er! — For
for a lov - er Hi - oh, The roll - ing riv - er! — She

take her 'cross the roll - ing wa - ter, Ha, ha! I'm bound a -
sev'n long years I court - ed Nan - cy, Ha, ha! I'm bound a -
would not have me for a lov - er, Ha, ha! I'm bound a -

1.-2.

way for the wide Mis - sour - i. 2. For
way for the wide Mis - sour - i. 3. She
way for the wide Mis -

3.

sour - i.

4. And so she took my fif-teen dol-lars, Hi - oh, The
5. (And) then she went to Kan-sas Cit - y, Hi - oh, The
6. (She) must have had an-oth-er lov-er, Hi - oh, The

roll-ing riv-er,— And so she took my fif-teen dol-lars,
roll-ing riv-er,— And then she went to Kan-sas Cit-y,
roll-ing riv-er,— She must have had an-oth-er lov-er,

Ha, ha! I'm bound a-way for the wide Mis-sour-i. 5. And
Ha, ha! I'm bound a-way for the wide Mis-sour-i. 6. She
Ha, ha! I'm bound a-way for the wide Mis- sour-i.

154

De Boatman's Dance
(Ohio)

Cheerful and in good rhythm, like a rustic dance

1. High row, the boat-men row, float-in' down the riv-er, the O-hi-o!
2. High row, the boat-men row, float-in' down the riv-er, the O-hi-o!

The boat-man dance, the boat-man sing, The boat-man up to ev-'ry-thing,
The boat-man is a thrift-y man, There's none can do as the boat-man can, Nev-er

When the boat-man gets on shore, He spends his mon-ey and works for more.
see a pret-ty gal in my life, But that she was a boat-man's wife.

Refrain

Dance the boat-man dance, Oh, dance the boat-man dance, Oh,

dance all night, till broad day light, Go home with the gals in the morn-ing.

Down the River
(Ohio)

A. W. Mason

With simplicity, and not fast

1. Oh, the riv-er is up, and the chan-nel is deep, And the wind blows stead-y and
2. Oh, the wa-ter is bright and flash-ing like gold In the ray of the morn-ing
3. Oh, the mas-ter is proud of the old Broadhorn, For it brings him plen-ty of
4. Oh there's plen-ty on board for the dark-ies to eat, And there's some-thing to drink and to

strong;— Let the splash of your oars the mea-sure keep, As we row the old boat a-long.
sun;— And old Di-nah's a-way, up out of the cold, A-get-ting the hoe corn done.
tin;— Oh, the crew they are darkies, the car-go is corn, And the mon-ey comes tum-bling in.
smoke;—There's the ban-jo, the bones and the tam-bour-ine, There's the song and the com-i-cal joke.

cresc.

Refrain (*ponderously*)

Down the riv-er, Down the riv-er, Down the riv-er we go.

mf deciso

Down the riv-er, Down the riv-er, Down the O-hi-o.

Eliza's Flight

(Ohio, 1852)

This song, inspired by Harriet Beecher Stowe's classic tale, was doubtless sung more than once by the soloists of the traveling "Uncle Tom's Cabin" companies.

Words by Miss M. A. Collier
Music by E. J. Loder

Pathetically but not too slow

1. The ice is float-ing in the stream, The win-try day is wild; Hope lights with her un-dy-ing gleam The wand-'rer and her child. She clasps him close-ly to her heart, Her on-ly one, her joy; For nought but death the two shall part, The

2. She press-es on, she press-es on, Nor heeds the i-cy flood; Thus on-ly may her rest be won, So help her, might-y God! The moth-er gains the fur-ther shore, Her babe is on her breast, The race is past, the per-il o'er, One

mother and her boy! She sees the cold and
mo-ment is she blest, Thus on-ly may her

rush-ing tide, Her feet are bleed-ing bare, She
rest be won, So help her, might-y God. The

lin-gers not, nor turns a-side, Yet breathes one heart-felt pray'r, She
moth-er gains the fur-ther shore, Her babe is on her breast, The

lin-gers not, nor turns a-side, Yet breathes one heart felt pray'r.—
race is past, the per-il o'er, One mo-ment is she blest.—

The Glendy Burke

(Ohio, 1860)

Stephen C. Foster

Very brightly

mf

1. De Glen - dy Burke is a
2. De Glen - dy Burke has a

might - y fast boat, wid a might - y fast cap - tain too; He
fun - ny old crew, and dey sing de boat - man's song; Dey

sets up dar on de hur - ri - cane roof, And he keeps his eye on de
burn de pitch an' de pine knot too, For to shove de boat a -

crew. I can't stay here, for de work's too hard, I'm ___
long. De smoke goes up an' de in - jine roars, An' de

bound   to   leave   dis   town;   I'll   take   my   duds   an'
wheel   goes   round   an'   round;   So   fare   ye   well,   for I'll

tote 'em   on   my   back, When   de   Glen - dy   Burke comes down.
take   a   lit - tle   ride, When   de   Glen - dy   Burke comes down.

Refrain

Ho!   for Lou' - si - an - a!   I'm   bound   to   leave   this   town;   I'll

take my duds an'   tote 'em on my back, When de   Glen - dy Burke comes down.

Gumbo Chaff

(Ohio)

Easily, but not too fast

1. On the O - hi - o bluff, in de
2. Once up - on a drift log think I
3. When de sun gone down, an' my

State of In - di - an - a, Dar's whar I used lib,— chock up in de har - bor
see an al - li - ga - tor, Skull my boat round den I— chuck him sweet po - tat - er;
day's work- o - ber, Ole Gum - bo Chaff he— tinks he libs in clo - ber,

Eb - 'ry morn - in' ear - ly, mas - sa gibs me li - quor, Take my
Hit him on de head, an' I try for to wix it, Could - n't
I gwan a - board de boat, wid my old tam - bor - in, Den

net an' pad - dle, an'— I— put out— quick - er, An' I
fool him bad, no— how— I could— fix it, So I
shub de boat orf and— gwan— to Or - le - an An' de

162

jump   in de skiff,   den I   row de rib - ber driff,   An' I
up   wid a brick,   an' I   fotch— such a lick,   But it
cap - tain dod rot 'em, Oh, I   neb - er will for - got 'em, For he

cotch as man - y tur - o - pins as   we two nig - gas lif'.
was— noth - in' but a pine - knot 'pon a big   stick.
put me on the leb - ee dar to   roll a bale o' cot - ton.

Ida May

(Ohio)

Percy St. Clair
J.J. Johnston

Sadly and slowly

1. Down by the banks of the O - hi - o, I was hap-py as the day,
2. (On a) bal - my — eve at sum-mer tide, For years had passed a - way, I

No care or sor - row did I know, For I loved sweet I - da May, Her
wan-der'd — by the riv - er side, Where my dar - ling I - da May, On

eyes shone bright as the eve - ning star, The voice of — sil - v'ry tone; I —
earth, death's hand — had chill'd our love, Still yet I'll — not des - pair, I —

long'd that the day — was not far, When I should say — my own, I
feel she is gone to dwell a - bove, We shall meet a - gain — up there, I

long'd that the day⌣ was not far, When⌣ I ⌣ should say my own.
feel she is gone to dwell a - bove, We shall meet⌣ a - gain up there.

Refrain

mf with expression

I - da May, I love thee, To my vows, dear I - da, hark - en,

ten.

Mine for - ev - er⌣ thou will be, Our love, no sor - row dark - en,

f *ten.*

Mine for - ev - er thou wilt be, Our love no sor - row dark - en. 2. On a dark - en.

mf *mp* *p*

1. 2.

Nancy Till

(Ohio, 1851)

With pastoral tenderness

1. Down in the cane - brake, close by the mill.
2. O - pen the win - dow, love Oh do!
3. Fare well love, I must now a - way. I've a

There lived a yel - low girl, her name was Nan - cy Till. She
And list - en to the mu - sic that I play for you. The
long way to trav - el be - fore the break of day. The

knew that I lov'd her, she knew it long, I'm
whis - p'rings of love, so soft and low, I'll
next time I come, be read - y, love, to go, A -

goin' to ser - e - nade her and I'll sing this song.
har - mo - nize my voice with the old ban - jo.
sail - ing on the banks of the O - hi - o.

Refrain

Come, love, come, the boat lies low, She lies high and dry on the O - hi - o; Come, love, come, won't you Come a - long with me? I'll take you down to Ten - nes see.

On the Banks of the Ohio

1. I asked my love to take a walk, Just to be a-lone with
2. (I asked your) moth-er for you, dear, And she said you were too
3. (I drew a) knife a-cross her breast, In my arms she dear-ly
4. (I took her) by her pale white hand, Led her to the riv-er
5. (Go-ing home) be-tween twelve and one, Think-ing of the deed I'd

me, And as we walked we'd have a talk, A-bout our wed-ding day to be.
young; On-ly say that you'll be mine, Hap-pi-ness in my home you'll find.
pressed, Cry-ing "Oh, please don't mur-der me, For I'm un-pre-pared to die.
brink: There I threw her in to drown, Stood and watched her float down.
done, I killed the on-ly girl I loved, Be-cause she would not mar-ry me.

Refrain

Oh, dar-ling, say that you'll be mine, In no one's arms I will you find Down be-

side dark wa-ters flow On the banks of the O-hi-o.

2. I asked your
3. I drew a
4. I took her
5. Go-ing home

The Unconstant Lover

(Ohio)

With simplicity

1. Oh — come, all my young lov-ers, Whom-so-ev-er wants to go— And we'll
2. (And)— we'll chaw our ter-back-er And— smoke our— pipe, And—

all set-tle down— On the O - hi - o. 2. And— 3. Now a
eat our per-ta-ties, When so - ev-er they gits ripe. 4. ('Cos a)

meet-in' are a pleas-ure, An' a par-tin' are a grief;— But an
thief he will— rob you Of— all that you— have;— But an

un-con-stant lov-er Is— wuss-er nor a thief. 4.'Cos a
un-con-stant lov-er Will— bring you to the grave.—

We'll Hunt the Buffalo

(Ohio)

As if sounding a hunter's horn

1. Come, all you brisk young fel-lows, who have a mind to roam Un-
2. (Come,) all ye pret-ty fair maids, and spin_ us some yarn, To
3. (There are) fish-es in the riv-er just fit-ted for our use; There's
4. (If) ev-er those wild In-dians do un-to us come nigh, We will

to some for-eign coun-try, a long way from home; Un-
make us some nice cloth-ing, to keep our-selves warm; For
tall and loft-y su-gar cane that yields us some juice; There
all u-nite to-geth-er, lads, to con-quer or die; We will

to some for-eign coun-try, a-long with me to go, And we'll
you can knit and sew, my loves, while we do reap and mow, When we
is all kind of game, my boys, be-side the buck and doe, When we
march in-to their tents, boys, and strike the dead-ly blow, When we

set-tle on the banks of the love-ly O-hi-o!
set-tle on the banks of the love-ly O-hi-o!
set-tle on the banks of the love-ly O-hi-o!
set-tle on the banks of the love-ly O-hi-o!

Refrain *(pompously)*

Sweet and sha-dy groves! Through the wild woods we'll wan-der, and we'll

hunt the Buf-fa-lo, And we'll hunt the Buf-fa-lo, Through the

wild woods we'll wan-der, and we'll hunt the Buf-fa-lo.

1.-2.-3.

4.

2. Come
3. There are
4. If

The Buffalo Skinners

(Pease)

This song appears in *Singing Cowboy*, by Margaret Larkin and H. Black as well as in *American Ballads and Folk Songs*, by John A. Lomax and Alan Lomax and in *The American Songbag*, by Carl Sandburg, etc.

Roughly

1. 'Twas in the town of Jacks-bo-ro, in eigh-teen eigh-ty three, A man by the name of Cre-go, Came step-ping up to me, Say-ing How do you do, young fel-low And how would you like to go,— And spend one sum-mer sea-son on the range of the buf-fa-lo.—

2. It's now our out-fit was com-plete, sev-en a-ble-bod-ied men, With na-vy six and nee-dle gun Our trou-bles did be-gun, Our way it was a pleas-ant one, The route we had to go,— Un-til we crossed Pease River on the range of the buf-fa-lo.—

3. It's now we crossed Pease riv-er, Our trou-bles have be-gun, The first damned tail I went to rip, Christ! how I cut my thumb. While skin-ning the damned old stink-ers, Our lives was not a show, For the In-dians watched to pick us off, While skinning the buf-fa-lo.—

4. He fed us on such sor-ry chuck I wished my-self most dead, It was old jerked beef, cro-ton cof-fee and sour bread. Pease Riv-er's salt-y as hell fire The wa-ter I could never go,— Oh, God I wished I'd nev-er come to the range of the buf-fa-lo.—

Driving Saw-logs on the Plover

This river takes its name from the Wisconsin village of Plover, the point at which it flows into the Wisconsin.

Wistfully

1. There walked on Plov - er's
2. "Why did - n't you stay up -
3. A log ca - noe came
4. Now all young men take

shad - y banks, One eve - ning last Ju - ly, ___ A moth - er of a
on the farm, And feed the ducks and hens, ___ And drive the pigs and
float - ing A - down the qui - et stream, ___ As peace - ful - ly it
this ad - vice: If e'er you wish to roam, ___ Be sure and kiss your

shan - ty boy, And dole - ful was her cry, ___ Say - ing:
sheep each night And put them in their pens? ___ Far
glid - ed As some young lov - er's dream. ___ A
moth - ers, Be fore you leave your home. ___ You had

173

"God be with you, John - nie, Al - though you're far a - way,— Driv-ing
bet - ter for you to help your dad To cut his corn and hay— Than to
youth crept out up - on the bank And thus to her did say,— "Dear—
bet - ter work up - on a farm For half a dol - lar a day— Than to

saw - logs on the Plo - ver, And you'll nev - er get your pay."—
drive saw - logs on the Plo - ver, And you'll nev - er get your pay."—
moth - er, I have jumped the game, And I have - n't got my pay!"—
drive saw - logs on the Plo - ver, And you'll nev - er get your pay.—

Red River Shore

Softly and naturally

1. At the foot of yon moun-tain, where the
2. (I) spoke to her kind-ly, say-ing
3. (I) asked her old fa-ther, if he'd

p *legato*

foun-tain doth flow, The great-est cre-a-tion, where the soft wind doth
"Will you mar-ry me? My for-tune's not great." "No mat-ter" said
give her to me. "No, sir, she shan't mar-ry no cow-boy," said

blow, There lived a fair maid-en, She's the one I a-dore; She's the
she. "Your beau-ty's a-plen-ty, You're the one I a-dore; You're the
he. So I jumped on my bron-co and a-way I did ride A-

ten.

1.-2.   3.

one I will mar-ry on the Red Riv-er shore. 2. I   4. She
one I will mar-ry on the Red Riv-er shore." 3. I   5. (So)
leav-ing my true love on the Red Riv-er side. 6. (I)

wrote me a let - ter, and she wrote it so kind, And in
I jumped on my bronc and a - way I did ride, To
drew my six - shoot - er, spun a - round and a - round, Till

this let - ter these words you could find, "Come
mar - ry my true love on the Red Riv - er side, But her
six men were wound - ed and sev - en were down, No

back to me, dar - ling: You're the one I a - dore You're the
dad knew the se - cret and with twen - ty and four, Came to
use for an ar - my of twen - ty and four, I'm

one I would mar - ry on the Red Riv - er shore. 5. So
fight this young cow - boy on the Red Riv - er shore. 6. I
bound for my true love on the Red Riv - er shore.

Red River Valley

Broadly

1. From this valley they say you are
2. (For a) long time I have been
3. (Won't you) think of the valley you're

mp

go - ing,_____ We will miss your bright eyes and sweet
wait - ing,_____ For those dear words you nev - er would
leav - ing?_____ Oh how lone - ly, how sad it will

smile, For they say you are tak - ing the sun - shine,_____ That
say, But at last all my fond hopes have van - ished,_____ For
be, Oh_____ think of the fond heart you're break - ing,_____ And the

1. - 2.

bright - ens our path - way a - while._____ 2. For a
they say you're go - ing a - way._____ 3. Won't you
grief you are caus - ing me to

3.

4. As you
5. (Come and)

see._____

go to your home by the o-cean,___ May you nev-er for-get those sweet
sit by my side if you love me,___ Do not hast-en to bid me a-

hours, That we spent in Red Riv-er Val-ley,___ And the
dieu, But re-mem-ber the Red Riv-er Val-ley,___ And the

love we ex-changed'mid the flow'rs.___ 5. Come and
cow-boy that loved you so true.___

5. Come and

The Ogallaly Song

(Republican)

This account of a long drive emphasizes the fact that the western rivers were landmarks by which the cowboys might register their progress. It is attributed to the Republican River. E. C. Abbott ("Teddy Blue") reports in *We Pointed Them North* (written in collaboration with Helena Huntington Smith) that the first time he remembered hearing this song "was one night in '81, on the Cimarron," where thirteen herds were camped "and you could count their fires."

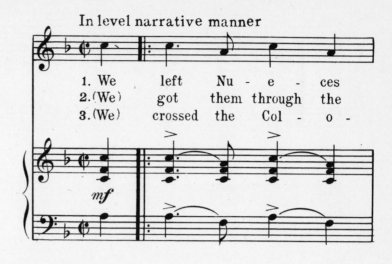

In level narrative manner

1. We left Nu - e - ces
2. (We) got them through the
3. (We) crossed the Col - o -

Riv - er in Ap - ril, eight - y - one, With the
brush all right, clear up to San An - tone, We
ra - do at Aus - tin, a big town, And

thou - sand long - horned cat - tle And all they knowed was
got some grub and head - ed north, As slick as an - y
head - ed north un - til we struck The store of big re -

piu espr.

| 1.-2. | 3 |

run, O - o - o - o - o - oh! 2. We 4. The
bone, O - o - o - o - o - oh! 3. We 5. (Then)
nown, O - o - o - o - o - oh! 6.

mp poco rit.   *p piu rit.*   *mf*   *mf*

Wash-i-ta was run-ning full, We got them all a-cross, And
we got to the old Dodge Cit-y on the Ar-kan-saw, Got a
On the Re-pub-lic-an___ We got an-oth-er storm, The

count-ed out on the oth-er bank, And nev-er had a
few drinks and got some more good grub And pulled out north once
boss he says this is the darnd-est coun-try I've seen since I was

loss, O - o - o - o - o - oh!
more, O - o - o - o - o - oh! 5. Then
born, O - o - o - o - o - 6. ___ oh!

piú espr.

mp poco rit.   *p piú rit.*   *mf*   *pp*

Ped.   *

This is a song of the forty-niners yearning for a
glimpse of the golden sands. It was used as a
sea chantey on sailing vessels going around the
Horn.

With strong, swinging rhythm

1. Oh say was you ev-er in Ri-o Grande, A-
2. It's fare-well to you, all you girls of the town, A-
3. Oh, John-ny came o-ver the oth-er day, A-
4. Now give me your hand, my dear lil-y white, A-
5. Now John-ny, I love you, don't want you to go, A-

way you Ri-o! It's there that the riv-er brings
way you Ri-o! You've got our half pay for to
way you Ri-o! Oh, John-ny came o-ver the
way you Ri-o! If you will ac-cept me I'll
way you Ri-o! And if you stay I will

down gold-en sand, For we're bound for the Ri-o Grande.
keep you a-round, For we're bound for the Ri-o Grande.
oth-er day, For we're bound for the Ri-o Grande.
make you my wife, For we're bound for the Ri-o Grande.
love you so, For we're bound for the Ri-o Grande.

An' a-way___ Ri - o, A - way___ you Ri - o,___ Sing
fare___ you well,___ my bon - ny young girl, For we're bound for the Ri - o Grande!___

The Silv'ry Rio Grande

With warmth

1. In the Lone Star State of Tex-as, by the sil-v'ry Ri - o Grande, Strolled a
2. (To_) Eur-ope she was go-ing, to be-come a la-dy grand, Where her
3. (My_) heart's to-night in Tex-as, though I'm far a-cross the sea, For the

cou-ple one fine eve-ning, two sweet-hearts hand in hand, 'Twas the
fa-ther hoped some Earl_ or else Count she'd_ wed, She_
band is play-ing Dix - ie, and it's there I long to be, Dad_

ranch-man's pret-ty daugh-ter and the lad she loved so dear, On the
left the ranch next morn-ing, though her heart was true to Jack, On-ly
says some Earl I'll mar - ry, but you shall have my hand, For my

mor - row they must part For man-y a wear-y year. 2. To_ 4. In a
yes - ter-day a let-ter came And this is what it said. 3. "My_ 5. ("I—)
heart's to-night in Tex - as By the sil-v'ry Ri - o Grande." 6. ("My_)

poco rit e dim.

mp

183

state - ly hall in Eng-land stood the Tex-as girl one night, The __
can't say yes" she an-swered, "Your ti - tle can-not take, There's a
heart's to - night in Tex - as, though I'm far a-cross the sea, Where the

scene was one of splen-dor and the lights were burn-ing bright, Be -
lad a - way in Tex - as, they call him Tex - as Jake, It is
band is play-ing Dix - ie, it's there I long to be, Dad

fore her knelt an Earl __ hum - bly beg-ging for her hand, But her
long a - go I prom-ised, that Tex - as lad to wed, On - ly
says some Earl I'll mar - ry but you shall have my hand, For my

4.-5. **6.**

thoughts were back in Tex - as By the sil-v'ry Ri - o Grande. 5. "I __
yes - ter - day I wrote, And it is thus the let-ter read." 6. "My __
heart's to - night in Tex - as By the sil-v'ry Ri - o Grande."

poco rit e dim

This song sung to an adaptation of Stephen Foster's "Camptown Races" was very popular with the forty-niners as they made their way westward to the California gold mines.

On the Banks of the Sacramento
(Circa 1850)

Tune: "Camptown Races"
by Stephen C. Foster

A bul-ly ship and a bul-ly crew, Doo-da, doo-da, A bul-ly mate and a cap-tain too, Doo-da, doo-da day! Then blow ye winds, hi-oh, For Cal-i-for-ny oh! There's plen-ty of gold, So I've been told, On the banks of Sac-ra-men-to!

Will You Come to the Bow'r?

(San Antonio, circa 1807)

Davy Crockett is said to have begun singing this when the Mexican attack on the Alamo began. A few months later Texan forces going into battle at San Jacinto were spurred to revenge by the sound of a single fife and drum playing "Will You Come to the Bow'r?"

Music by "T. M. Esq.ʳ"

Gracefully, but not fast

mf

1. Will you come to the bow'r I have shad-ed for you? Our bed shall be ros-es all span-gled with dew. Will you come to the bow'r I have shad-ed for you, Our bed shall be ros-es All span-gled with dew.

2. There un-der the bow'r on ros-es you'll lie, With a blush on your cheek, but a smile in your eye. There un-der the bow'r in ros-es you'll lie, With a blush on your cheek But a smile in your eye.

186

Will you, will you, will you, will you come to the bow'r?
Will you, will you, will you, will you smile, my be-lov'd?

Will you, will you, will you, will you, come to the bow'r?
Will you, will you, will you, will you, smile, my be lov'd?

The Wyandotte's Farewell Song

(Sandusky)

With solemnity, almost religiously

1. A - dieu to the graves_ where my fa - thers now rest! For I must be go - ing a - far to the West; I've sold my pos - ses - sions, my heart's filled with woe, To think I must lose— them, A - las! I must go.

2. Fare - well, ye tall oaks,— in whose pleas - ant green shade In child - hood I ram - bled, in in - no - cence played; My dog and my hatch - et, my ar - rows and bow, Are still in re - mem - brance, A - las! I must go.

3. San - dus - ky, Ty - mock - tee and Brock - en - sword streams Nev - er - more I shall see— you ex - cept in my dreams A - dieu to the marsh - es where cran - ber - ries grow, O'er great Mis - sis - sip - pi, A - las! I must go.

4. Fare - well, my white friends_ who first taught me to pray And wor - ship my Mak - er and Sa - viour each day, Oh, pray for the na - tive whose eyes o - ver - flow, With tears at our part - ing, A - las! I must go.

From *Ballads and Songs from Ohio*, copyright, 1939, by Mary O. Eddy, and reprinted by her permission.

El-a-noy
(Wabash)

Moderately slow

1. Way down—up-on the Wa-bash Sich land was nev-er known; If
2. 'Twas here—the Queen of She-ba came, With Sol-o-mon of old, With an
3. She's bound-ed by the Wa-bash, The O-hi-o and the Lakes, She's

Ad-am had passed o-ver it The soil he'd sure-ly own; He'd
ass—load of spic-es, Pome-gran-ates and fine gold; And
craw-fish in the swamp-y lands, The milk-sick and the shakes; But

think it was the gar-den He'd played in when a boy, And
when she saw this love-ly land, Her heart was filled with joy, Straight-
these are slight di-ver-sions And take not from the joy Of

straight pro-nounce it E-den, In the State of El-a-noy.
way she said "I'd like to be A Queen in El-a-noy."
liv-ing in this gar-den land, The State of El-a-noy.

From *The American Songbag*, compiled by Carl Sandburg, copyright, 1927, by
Harcourt, Brace & Company, Inc., and reprinted by their permission.

Refrain

Then move your fam-'ly west-ward, Good health you will en - joy, And

rise to wealth and hon- or In the State of El - a - noy.___

mf a tempo

_p_

190

Way Down in the Paw-Paw Patch

(Wabash)

Gracefully

1. Where, oh, where is sweet lit-tle Bet-ty, Where, oh, where is
2. Come on, boys, and let's go find her, Come on, boys, and
3. Pick up paw-paws, put 'em in a bas-ket, Pick up paw-paws,

mf

sweet lit-tle Bet-ty, Where, oh, where is sweet lit-tle Bet-ty?
let's go find her, Come on, boys, and let's go find her,
put 'em in a bas-ket, Pick up paw-paws, put 'em in a bas-ket,

Way down yon-der in the paw-paw patch.
Way down yon-der in the paw-paw patch.
Way down yon-der in the paw-paw patch.

f

On the Banks of the Little Eau Pleine

(Wisconsin)

1. The sun in the west was de - clin - ing, And tinge - ing the tree tops with red, My wan - d'ring feet bore me on - ward, Not car - ing whith - er they

2. Say - ing, "A - las dear John - ny has left me, I'm a - fraid I shall see him no more He's down on the low - er Wis - con - sin, He's pull - ing a fif - ty foot

3. I stepped up be - side this young school ma'am, And thus un - to her I did say, "Why is it you're mourn - ing so sad - ly, While all na - ture is smil - ing and

4. "If John Mur - phy's the name of your rafts - man, I used to know him ver - y well, But sad is the tale I must tell you, Your John - ny was drowned in the

5. "My curs - es at - tend you Wis - con - sin, May your ra - pids and falls cease to roar, May ev - 'ry tow - head and sand - bar Be as dry as a log school - house

led._____ I hap - pened to see a young
oar._____ He went off on a fleet with Ross
gay?"_____ She said "It is for a young
Dells._____ They bur - ied him 'neath a scrub
floor,_____ May the wil - lows up - on all your

school ma'am,_____ She mourned in a sor - row - ful
Gam - ble,_____ And has left me in sor - row and
rafts - man,_____ For whom I so sad - ly com -
Nor - way,_____ You will nev - er be - hold him a -
is - lands,_____ Lie down like a field of ripe

strain,_____ She mourned for a jol - ly young rafts - man,_____
pain,_____ And 'tis o - ver two months since he start - ed,_____
plain,_____ He has left me a - lone here to wan - der,_____
gain,_____ No stone marks the spot where your rafts - man,_____
grain,_____ For tak - ing my jol - ly young rafts - man,_____

On the banks of the Lit - tle Eau Pleine._____
From the banks of the Lit - tle Eau Pleine."_____
On the banks of the Lit - tle Eau Pleine."_____
Sleeps far from the Lit - tle Eau Pleine."_____
A - way from the Lit - tle Eau Pleine."_____

Index of Titles

Index of First Lines